M000097094

A Stranger Truth

A Stranger Truth

Lessons in Love, Leadership and Courage
from India's Sex Workers

Ashok Alexander

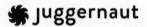

JUGGERNAUT BOOKS
KS House, 118 Shahpur Jat, New Delhi 110049, India

First published by Juggernaut Books 2018

The international boundaries on the maps of India are neither purported to be correct nor authentic by Survey of India directives.

10 9 8 7 6 5 4 3 2 1

ISBN 9788193876701

Typeset in Adobe Caslon Pro by R. Ajith Kumar, Noida

Printed at Manipal Technologies Limited, Manipal

To the communities who made it all possible

Contents

x　　　　　　　　　　Contents

Introduction

In April 2003 I left a long career at McKinsey and Company, the venerable global management consultancy, to take up an invitation from the Bill & Melinda Gates Foundation to create a programme to stem the growth of HIV across India. HIV prevalence was high and climbing in several parts of the country, and there were fears across the world that India's epidemic could spiral out of control. The Indian government was in denial. Something had to be done.

That I knew virtually nothing about HIV or public health didn't deter me. McKinsey people, it is sometimes said, combine amazing cockiness with a certain deep insecurity. When I started out I felt self-assured, perhaps to the point of cockiness, with just that tinge of nervous excitement that comes at the start of any new venture. I thought I would quickly have HIV all figured out, just as quickly as we had figured out new client businesses. Of course, a rude awakening was to follow, a sobering experience I will describe later in the book. But to start with, at least, I did the sensible thing and set out for the field to acquaint myself with the fundamentals.

I thought I was taking up a new career. I didn't expect I would also be plunged into an adventure that was both bewildering and exhilarating. It led me to visit places and get to know people I'd never imagined existed. It was an India that fell outside the comfort

1

zones I had lived and worked in all my life. It went beyond the brief encounters with poverty I had seen from so many windows. It was a grinding place where women would sell themselves for fifty rupees and fourteen-year-olds injected drugs. It was the secret world of transgender people, and the agony of young gay men in a country that still criminalized same-sex love. It was the strange world of truckers, lonely journeymen along forgotten highways. It also often turned out to be a place of spectacular natural beauty. It was, above all, a place where heroic battles for a barely decent life were being fought every day.

$\sim$

I began to build a team, and we gave our programme the name Avahan, meaning 'clarion call'. It seemed apt, given the prevailing environment of denial. Our game plan was to concentrate on the six states where HIV levels were the highest in India. These were Nagaland and Manipur in the North-East; Andhra Pradesh (as it was then called),[1] Karnataka, and Tamil Nadu in the South; and Maharashtra in the west. We chose these states because they accounted for the bulk of new HIV infections and because HIV prevention measures there were inadequate. Within these states we would focus on eighty-three (virtually all) districts and establish operations in hundreds of towns.

The central theme of Avahan therefore was achieving very large scale in a very short period, for maximum impact. But the essence of Avahan, and the purpose of this book, is the power of communities. It is the story of the strength inherent in even the most marginalized of people, if they are enabled to come together in common cause. Sex workers across Avahan's six states, with adequate initial support, developed and implemented sophisticated solutions to generate data, deliver services based on that data, and reduce their vulnerability.

The word community will come up throughout this narrative. It refers to the people who belong to different population groups most at risk of getting infected by the HIV virus. The largest such group was that of female sex workers. There were also men who have sex with men ('MSM', which is different from 'gay', and we will see why later in the book); transgender people; truckers – who often are clients of sex workers; and injecting drug users. There are subcategories within these groups – especially with the female sex workers. These risk groups were often widely dispersed and moving around in a way that made them invisible. That was one of the biggest challenges in expanding our programme to reach the population groups most vulnerable to HIV.

As this strange adventure unfolded, I would at the end of the day often ask myself – did that really happen today? I decided to keep a daily record of my travels, thinking that otherwise no one, including myself, would believe that this was truth, not fiction. These regular writings grew into two thick, handwritten diaries that chronicle most of the ten years I spent on Avahan. As I look through this journal today I am struck by the detail – people, places, and conversations – put down literally, and without embellishment. Without these diaries this book would not have been possible.

In many instances, the names of people, and sometimes the places or the dates, have been changed. I use the first-person style through most of this narrative because it is my personal story, and I cannot speak for the thoughts and emotions of my colleagues as we made the journey together. I had the added good fortune, by being the captain of the ship, to be the only person who worked right across Avahan and could visit every state and locale and engage with each of the diverse communities I met. The first-person device should never disguise the fact that Avahan was entirely a team game – the core Avahan team, the teams of the NGOs that implemented the programme, and the communities involved.

This is not a technical book which gets into the details of the methods we followed in rapidly expanding Avahan. It doesn't get into areas such as how we went about monitoring and evaluating our progress, fascinating though they are. It doesn't discuss what it took to build a high-performing team. Avahan is a well-documented programme, with case studies and hundreds of peer-reviewed articles.

This is essentially a narrative about a personal journey, engaging only lightly with technicalities.

The book is in two sections. In part 1, 'Far, Far Away', I try to depict the many settings in which HIV is transmitted, based on my field travels across India. I describe the various communities and introduce some of the characters I met during my travels. It provides the canvas, describes the challenges, and touches on the elements of the solution we developed.

Part 2, 'Learning to Fly', is set in Mysore, focusing on the part of the Avahan programme that was set up there, called Ashodaya, built by sex workers. It is a deep dive into how Avahan worked at the grass roots. If part 1 lays out the nature of the problem, part 2 tries to convey the character of the solution.

The appendix contains some background on HIV globally and in India, and is worth skimming through after reading this Introduction, especially by those new to the HIV world.

～

Today, with the advent of treatment, a person with HIV can expect to live a long and normal life. This was not the case for most of the period in which we worked on Avahan. Treatment was barely available then in India, and contracting the virus was tantamount to a cruel death sentence. Over a period of about ten years the victim would progress into the AIDS stage, when his immune system collapsed, and death would come, slowly and painfully.

Working on Avahan, seeing this tragedy happen up-close, changed me fundamentally. I found I was able to feel, rather than intellectualize or turn away when faced with suffering. I became better able to face my fears, and to understand what made me happy. I discovered a self that had long been buried within. Perhaps this book may provoke a few readers to reflect on the forces that bind them to one place or to one attitude, or to wonder whether they may be staying on a little too long, without intending to do so, in their zones of comfort. In so reflecting they may, like me, discover some emotions, long suppressed, well concealed, worthy of expression.

I hope this book may also, for those who sense a restlessness deep within, stoke the fires of the adventures waiting to be had, the quiet clarion call, the call to make a difference.

Part I
Far, Far Away

Far, far away, someone was weeping,
but the world was sleeping,
Any dream will do.

– Andrew Lloyd Webber and Timothy Rice

1

First Night Out

'Don't step on the people having sex . . .' the NGO worker whispered urgently as we ventured into the darkness. I was in the heart of Visakhapatnam, a bustling port and steel city on the east coast of India. An open field about fifty yards square lay before us. Behind us lay Waltair Road, a long thoroughfare that bisects Vizag, as the city is fondly called. The bright orange lights of the port winked just beyond. Amongst rubble, shrubs, and occasional trees, dim, ghostlike figures convened in groups and in couples. The darkness was punctuated by the glow of cigarette butts, and the sea breeze occasionally carried the aromas of harsh tobacco, cheap perfume, and sweet night jasmine. The raucous noise coming from the road was extinguished by the silence of the field. I felt as if I had stumbled into a strange twilight zone.

The NGO working with sex workers in Vizag had set up an appointment for me to meet Parvati, Vatsala, and Jayanthi. Spotting us, they signalled that we walk across the field to join them where they were doing business. I could hear them giggle as they watched me move gingerly around the couples that lay strewn around the field. As we made our way across, I absorbed the scene around me. Every ten metres or so there were couples making introductions, others in the last stages of negotiation, and yet others engaged in writhing exploration. Sounds of frantic coitus emanated from behind bushes.

No one seemed to mind our presence. I stumbled, fortunately only on stones, as I stepped up to meet the three ladies of the night. They had on bright red, blue, and green polyester-silk saris with gold borders, and wore heavy make-up. I offered a self-conscious namaste. Our discussions didn't last very long. We had barely got beyond introductions when a few young men approached, keen to start talking business.

'How does all this go on in the heart of a big city, in conservative South India?' I asked my companion Sara Kurian, a young, idealistic, and overstretched NGO worker from Kerala employed by the organization that managed the government's HIV and AIDS programmes in Vizag. We had stepped back across the field, crossed Waltair Road, and within a few minutes entered the glare of downtown Vizag. Sara didn't answer directly. 'Would you like to meet the main external stakeholder?' she asked. Intrigued by her turn of phrase, I nodded yes.

She led me across the street to the brightly lit entrance of a coffee shop. Just next to the cafe was an innocuous paan kiosk. A sadhu with an ample frame, who looked in his fifties, with a thick beard and twirled moustaches, sat on a high chair flush against the kiosk, draped in saffron. An exaggerated amount of sacred ash was spread across his forehead. He motioned for us to approach. Here was the 'main external stakeholder' – a man of God, a businessman, and a super pimp. Heavy-lidded, dark, intense eyes bored into me. I felt a sense of power and malevolence. My clammy palms joined in greeting.

'How does all this go on? What about the police?' I asked cautiously, indicating the field hidden behind the shops across Waltair Road. 'I take care of everyone here,' he said. Though his demeanour radiated benediction, there was something lurking behind his eyes that I couldn't quite reach. 'Every single person you see around here,' he continued, gesturing with his hand as though to suggest the whole city. 'That includes the police, who are very happy and don't create a problem . . . but if they do then I take special care of them.' A weary, other-worldly smile crossed his lips.

As we prepared to leave, the sadhu's eyes caught mine, and he glanced down to his feet. Again, I felt a wave of quiet menace. Taking courage, I took leave without the expected touching of the feet of a holy man. With a quick namaste and dipping of head, I stepped back out into the world of tourists and small traders, and the riot of noise that is downtown Vizag.

~

I had left McKinsey a month earlier, captivated by an offer from the Bill & Melinda Gates Foundation to lead the creation of an HIV prevention programme that would help stem the spread of the epidemic in India. I had spent seventeen years by then in McKinsey and was a director (senior partner) in charge of its New Delhi office. McKinsey's clients included two-thirds of the Fortune 1000, as well as governments and non-profit institutions. McKinsey selected its people carefully and presented them with a career that was both exciting and demanding. Rewarding work, punishing travel, and a rigorous system of up or out were all part of the package. Most people spent less than four years at the Firm (as McKinsey refers to itself), such was the intensity of a career there.

I learnt how to crack difficult business problems at McKinsey. I knew how to identify the main issues behind a problem, break it into its parts, and put it all back together, in the form of a clear way forward. If a situation seemed unfamiliar, there was the vast storehouse of knowledge that came from the Firm's experience across the world.

These skills gave me a strong foundation, but I was soon to find out that they could take me only up to a point in my new career. Now, in my first foray into the field, I felt I was in some baffling dream, reality distorted, in a place I never knew existed, an invisible India. I already had a sense of plunging into the vast unknown, with no parachute, no map.

~

Later that night in Vizag, just behind a large cinema theatre, huddled in the tiny yard of an empty house on a side street, we met three women, old and emaciated, squatting on the ground. They were in tattered, threadbare saris and worn-out rubber chappals and presented a very different picture from the women I had met in the field a little earlier. Their sheer desolation struck me.

The yard was dark, illuminated only by a flickering light bulb on a lamp post just outside. The women brightened when they saw Sara, whom they obviously trusted. They listlessly received packets of condoms from Sara, who was talking to them in the local language, Telugu, all the time. It was evident they were not able to insist on the use of the condoms with the occasional clients they would encounter, too drunk to look into the sex workers' faces and recognize that these women were older than their mothers.

I asked, and was told that the transaction would cost from thirty to fifty rupees, or less, sometimes just enough for the next meal.

As though reading my mind, Sara said, 'It gets worse than this. There is a form of exploitation where brokers bring women into the city from the rural areas. The women usually do sex work for a few months, or maybe only a few weeks, to pay off a mounting debt, or deal with some pressing family need. They go back to the village after that. They may never practise sex work again.

'There are different formulas,' she continued in a matter-of-fact way, 'but typically, if a woman comes to the city for forty days, she will be paid eight thousand rupees by the end of that period. The agreement she has with the broker is that he can send her as many clients in a day as he can find. He takes fifty rupees from each client, and the woman gets nothing more than the daily two hundred rupees. If she doesn't get four clients in a day, it's not counted as a working day and she gets paid nothing. Sometimes the broker may send up to fifty clients in a day. Come, let me show this to you.'

I was not sure I wanted to see more, but Sara led us to a small, open space in the shadows behind some shops. Luckily, business was over for the day. The only evidence left was a charpoy with a torn blue tarpaulin over it, and a small hill of used condoms on the side.

'The men usually wait in line,' Sara said. 'They are very orderly.'

~

That visit to Vizag in December 2002 was my first field trip after taking on the new job with the Gates Foundation. The city, then with a population of about two million, dates to the sixth century CE. It is a big commercial hub, in constant churn. Thousands of men come in every week from neighbouring parts of the district in search of daily wages. They work in the massive steel plant or at the docks and live in the city's sprawling slums. Small businessmen from faraway towns down the coast come to Vizag to clinch crucial orders. Over two thousand trucks, and their drivers, halt at the giant truck stop on NH5[1] that runs along the coast, bypassing the main city. Lonely sailors from across the world drop anchor at Vizag and explore the teeming metropolis. Peasant women from distant villages arrive to sell their scanty yield on the weekly market day.

For all these reasons, paid-for sex thrives in Vizag. Commercial sex activity here is mostly the low-end street-based sex work that is the norm in towns all over India, practised behind bushes near deserted buildings, or further up the scale, in conveniently located lodges. Not surprisingly, Vizag at that time was also a hotbed for the spread of HIV. About two of every hundred adults in the city was HIV positive. The World Health Organization (WHO) defines a generalized epidemic as one that affects more than 2 per cent of the adult population.

But Vizag was not unique. The same story was being repeated in towns across India. In 2002 HIV affected an estimated 4.8 million[2] people in India, according to the estimates of the government's

National AIDS Control Organization (NACO). People were being newly infected in India at the rate of about a thousand every day. A particularly tragic aspect was the growing number of AIDS orphans, estimated at over two million, the largest such population in the world.

It takes a special type of person to serve at the front line of the campaign against HIV. My guide through the day, Sara Kurian was an outreach worker[3] – which meant she worked directly with sex workers in the field. She, like me, was from Kerala's Syrian Christian community which is highly tradition-bound. I couldn't understand how someone who was probably from a conservative family could spend her days with sex workers, telling them about the importance of safe sex, urging them to get treatment for sexually transmitted infections (STIs), always carrying a wooden penis model in her handbag to demonstrate how clients should wear condoms – because sex workers often have to do that with drunken patrons.

I asked her about this. 'It's simple – my family doesn't know,' said Sara. 'I studied in a small town in Kerala and always was keen on social work. Therefore, I did a master's in social work. My parents are proud of that and that I am working for a good NGO, but they don't know that I am working with sex workers. It would upset them a lot! They want to arrange a marriage for me with someone from a good family. If people came to know what I am really doing it will affect my [marriage] chances.' Sara said she hoped she would find a boy who supports her work, because she loves what she is doing and doesn't want to give it up.

We left for our last stop, the NGO's office in a suburb of Vizag.

~

The NGO's office was a modest three-room house, with peeling yellow plaster, in a middle-class residential area. Above the door was a blackboard with the words Mahila Purogati Samajam, which means Women's Progress Society, lettered on it in Telugu and English. A heap of chappals lay outside. A loud buzz of voices and bursts of raucous laughter came from a room down the corridor. I removed my shoes and stepped into the office.

I was nervous. I had never faced a group of sex workers before and wasn't quite sure what to say. Self-consciously I entered the small room, which had dark curtains on its two windows. There were no furnishings, except for a thin durrie on the ground. About twenty women, ranging from teenagers to some in their forties, were awaiting my arrival. A few in front wore bright silk saris and costume jewellery, obviously dressed up for the occasion. Others wore everyday clothes, mainly saris, some salwar kameez, one a burkha.[4] Against the wall at the back sat a few women who looked destitute, much like the three old women in the yard behind the movie theatre. Sara whispered to me that some of these women worked part-time on the NGO's HIV prevention programme.

The sex workers clapped their hands boisterously, and I folded my hands in namaste. For a laugh, I told them I was not a client, but I had come with some small gifts. I produced about a dozen of the red, ultra-thin, imported condoms I had been told sex workers valued, because they used them to entice their clients. I apologized, saying I didn't know that there would be so many of them there, and I didn't have enough for everyone. Someone shouted, 'Just throw them!' so I threw them up in the air. The women scrambled to get them, laughing, having mock fights, some grabbing two and pushing them down their blouses.

The ice had been broken and I was at ease. For the next hour the women told me about the extent to which they used condoms, how they found their clients, what they charged, the problems they faced with their regular boyfriends, and their dreams for their children. The women at the back kept their heads down and didn't say a word.

I asked one of the women in front, Rajamma, who looked about twenty-five, if she had ever been tested for HIV. 'I haven't,' she said quietly. 'Though it could well be that I am HIV positive, because I practised unsafe sex till very recently. I learnt about condoms only after coming across this programme.' I asked, 'Then why don't you get yourself tested? Isn't it better you know?'

'But what will happen if I know, and then everyone knows?' Rajamma said, looking straight into my eyes. 'I will lose my job, be thrown out of my home. Who will look after my child, who will pay for my treatment? It's very expensive.' I was at a loss for words. I muttered something about being willing personally to take care of all her costs. 'And will you take care of the testing, and the costs of all my sisters in this room, and will you take care of *all* the sex workers outside this room too?' she shot back, eyes flashing.

I felt ashamed. It would not be the last time a commercial sex worker would ask me a question in public to which I had no answer. As the meeting broke up, Rajamma approached me with a few others. I think they sensed my shame and feeling of inadequacy.

'Tomorrow is our annual picnic,' she said, to put me at ease. 'There will be more than two hundred of us taking buses to a scenic spot. It is organized by the NGO. Would you like to come? Just imagine what a great time you could have, just one man in such lovely company!' I smiled and said regretfully that I would have to pass on the offer this time. The women collapsed in shrieks of laughter.

~

I flew back to Delhi the next day, my thoughts aswirl. In just two weeks after I left the Firm and on my first night out, I had been transported into a strange new realm of hidden sex work in a field in Vizag, where a godman sold sex, old women offered themselves for almost nothing, lust-filled men stood in line, and sex workers dispensed wisdom.

2

Taking the Plunge

Bill Gates arrived in India on 11 November 2002 to a welcome that Indians reserve for very few visitors. The founder of Microsoft was an icon in a country that has information technology in its DNA. But this visit had little to do with business. Instead, it was about the Bill & Melinda Gates Foundation's work and the announcement of a $100 million[1] grant to tackle HIV in India.

Six weeks earlier, I had received a call from my fellow McKinsey partner Paul Jansen in San Francisco. 'Bill Gates will be coming to India to announce a massive grant to tackle HIV in India,' he said. 'They want some support organizing for the event. Can you guys help? The Gates Foundation is an important client.' When I asked Paul what kind of help they would need, he paused, as though that was a question he hadn't expected. 'Just some help with the arrangements,' he said vaguely. That sounded like an easy thing to do, and I assured Paul that we would make sure things went well. That innocuous phone call would change the course of my life forever.

Assuming that all that was needed was some straightforward help with logistics and setting up meetings, I decided to assign a couple of business analysts – the juniormost position in the Firm – to the project. But it turned out that all of them were already deployed. So

I decided to provide the help myself, in effect demoting myself from director to analyst.

A couple of staff from the foundation had already arrived in Delhi to set things up (in contrast with McKinsey, which referred to itself as 'the Firm' with a capital 'F', the Gates Foundation referred to itself as 'the foundation' with the 'f' in lower case). I learnt that the foundation planned to give the money to a single organization they called a 'contractor', which would make subgrants to different implementing agencies. The contractor would be managed from Seattle, but the choice had not yet been made. This remote-control idea seemed a bit odd.

Paul told me that the foundation had been thinking of an India AIDS grant for more than a year, talking to experts around the world, and they had come up with a strategy they called 'Men on the Move'. They would focus on groups of men who were away from home for long periods – such as migrants, truckers, and the armed forces – men who, being deprived for long periods, would frequent sex workers and have abundant unprotected sex with them. The reasoning was that getting those men to use condoms would be the best way to tackle HIV in India. Somehow, this approach seemed off the mark. I did some reading in the next few days about HIV prevention programmes.

~

Helene Gayle, head of HIV prevention and treatment at the foundation, directly responsible for the India grant, arrived in New Delhi a few days later. A tall African-American woman, a medical doctor and seasoned public health expert, Helene was an impressive personality. She was a good listener with a great sense of humour, and we connected immediately. I told her I had some questions about the strategy of focusing on the client of the sex worker. Every sex worker has tens of clients. Wouldn't it make more sense for the plan to focus on her rather than her clients?[2] The real problem would be how to do it on a scale larger than anything that had been attempted before.

That required intense management. I could not understand why the foundation was considering managing it all from far away. I remember saying: 'India is a complicated place. You can't just tell some contractor, "Here's a hundred million dollars, now go fix HIV in India."' Helene asked a few questions and said she could see the merit in what I was saying. She added that it ran contrary to the foundation's policy of not getting directly involved in implementation. Little did I know that this policy would be the bone I would choke on a little later.

Focus on the source, have local presence, think about how to scale up – it seemed straightforward. It struck me that not knowing much about HIV need not be a handicap. Helene and I talked about these ideas many times as she spent the week in India. She was meeting people, no doubt including those on the shortlist of possible candidates for consultant or agent.

Soon after she got back to Seattle, Helene sent me a message: 'Would you consider leading this initiative to stop AIDS in India? We'll back you all the way.' Till then, the idea of leaving McKinsey had never seriously crossed my mind, but at that moment something positive stirred within me. It was all so sudden, and I had no idea if the foundation's leadership was really committed. Helene must have read my thoughts because she said, 'Why don't you come over next week to the foundation and meet some of the folks there? See how you feel after that.' I readily agreed.

~

In October 2002 the Bill & Melinda Gates Foundation was housed in a grey concrete building with two floors, in a nondescript residential area of Seattle.[3] I was struck by the hush as soon as I stepped inside. People didn't congregate, they padded down corridors, they spoke softly, phones buzzed discreetly, everyone smiled warmly. Coming from the noise and bustle of India, it all struck me as being just so very calm, but in a slightly eerie way.

'You'll probably be meeting Bill as well today,' Helene had said when I checked in. I was taken aback. 'What should I wear?' were the foolish words that came out of my mouth. The answer was not reassuring: 'Anything, as long as you don't look like a consultant.' I wondered what else I could look like, after seventeen years with McKinsey.

My schedule had meetings with Bill Senior, Bill Gates's father; Patty Stonesifer, president of the foundation; and a group called the 'India Team'. Bill's name was not on the schedule anywhere.

~

The meeting room was small, with a polished walnut table that could take eight chairs. At one end of the room was a refrigerator stacked with an array of slightly offbeat sodas – stuff like Dr. Pepper, Cherry Coke, Fresca, and Canada Dry Ginger Ale – that seemed to have been carefully selected.

The foundation had a few research grants operating in India that were managed directly from Seattle. Some were focused only on India; in others, India was one of the countries in a multi-country grant. The grants worked through Indian government research agencies and a few biotech companies. Almost all had to do with the development of essential new vaccines. The meeting was for Bill to review progress on the foundation's work in India, on the eve of his visit.

Pleasantries and friendly banter were being exchanged inside the room, but there was an edge to it, some nervous laughter. Everyone was waiting. It struck me that each person had come prepared to say something of substance. They all had slides. I hadn't planned anything and carried no papers. Maybe I had just followed too literally Helene's advice not to act or look like a consultant!

Bill came in and went straight to the refrigerator to get himself a soft drink, without glancing at anyone. He was different from what I'd imagined, comfortably crumpled – loose sweater, corduroys, dishevelled hair. He carried a yellow A4-sized notepad, on which I noticed he scribbled notes with a cheap plastic pen throughout the meeting. The buzz in the room switched off as soon as he stepped in. An intense discussion followed as grants were reviewed in turn. Bill had a sardonic, throwaway sense of humour that surfaced regularly, though no one was laughing out loud. But his mood could change quickly, if something was falling short.

This vaccines review went on for most of the allotted hour. Some of the conversation was about certain massive investments supporting institutions such as IAVI (which worked on developing an AIDS vaccine), GAVI (promoting vaccines in general), and the Global Fund for HIV, Malaria and Tuberculosis. These were global institutions that had been set up through foundation funding.

The talk turned to Bill's forthcoming visit to India in two weeks. Bill wanted to know what each meeting would be about. I came in a few times, to clarify who some of the people were, or the political context. Bill's attitude was 'We don't understand how India works, we have a lot to learn', never 'look what we are doing for India'.

It dawned on me that so far the foundation had invested almost entirely in health products (vaccines mainly) or technologies, or the building of institutions to support this approach. The India HIV grant was a venture into an area the foundation was totally unfamiliar with – health service delivery on a massive scale, in a country where they had only a limited presence.

The meeting made a deep impression on me. I marvelled at the vast horizons that the team in that room was chasing with so much passion. Whether it was polio, HIV, guinea worm, or kala azar, the talk was about nothing less than total eradication. I could see that the India AIDS initiative, aiming to stem the growth of an epidemic that could devastate India, would be just as important to the foundation. Bill's concern and deep personal commitment were evident. I was in.

Why did I make such a radical shift in career? Above all, the sheer audacity of the proposition, the chance to create a programme to fight a virus that might endanger my country, was staggering. There was also the exhilaration of jumping into the great unknown and, yes, the misplaced conceit that I could save the world. I was gripped by all the possibilities of having an impact.

But there was also something else, which I can best describe as a quiet restlessness growing within me. I didn't realize it then, but I can see that clearly now. I had reached a peak in my career and had begun, subconsciously, to think about where I was heading. In rare moments of reflection, stripped of hubris, it was evident to me that much of what I had achieved came because of the privileges I had started out with.

Look in any direction in India, and we see inequality. Like many others, I too felt that one day I needed to give back. So far that had been an intrusive, inconvenient thought. There was always so much here and now to attend to, there would be a time later, after I left the Firm, to get to it. And now here was that unmistakable opportunity, presenting itself out of the blue, and suddenly I knew it would never come again. I found myself asking not 'What if I do this?' but 'What if I didn't do this?' and I realized that I would spend the rest of my life wondering what it would have been like if I had accepted the offer.

Therefore, many threads came together with the offer from the foundation, coming so suddenly in November 2002. I had no inkling, though, that I was crossing a line and I would never come back; and because of that seemingly chance phone call, my life would change forever.

～

Bill announced the Bill & Melinda Gates Foundation's India AIDS Initiative (we coined the name Avahan a few months later) at a crowded press conference hours after he arrived, and again that evening at a gala dinner. As camera bulbs flashed, he spoke of the foundation's concern about India's AIDS epidemic, the growing numbers of HIV cases, and his hope that the foundation could make a critical difference. 'In Ashok, we have someone who knows India and the world of business,' he said. 'We believe he will provide the right leadership for our initiative.' The response from the media the next morning was exultant. 'Gates Gives India More than Africa for AIDS' shouted the *Times of India*, grammar be damned. The *Indian Express* in a lead story wrote: 'Such philanthropy is not only unprecedented . . . [but is directed at] a sector that if not urgently attended to, could wipe out an enormous section of our working population'. The stately *New York Times*, however, had already detected 'a certain ambivalence on the government's side'.

Indeed, storm clouds were gathering. Some government bureaucrats had persuaded Health Minister Shatrughan Sinha that the foundation was exaggerating the threat of HIV and implying that not enough was being done by the government to tackle it. The foundation's decision to fund NGOs directly rather than work through the government was being questioned. The minister was a former Hindi movie star, popularly known as 'Shotgun'. He was not known for his thoughtfulness, and was naturally inclined towards histrionics. He called a hurried press conference. 'Mr Gates is spreading false alarm about HIV in India,' he thundered in his famous baritone. 'The figures he is citing about AIDS cases are a CIA fabrication.[4] We don't need his money. We can control HIV on our own in India.'

Hurriedly, I met with Meenakshi Datta-Ghosh, the senior bureaucrat who headed the National AIDS Control Organization, to ask that they rein in the bad-mouthing of the Gates Foundation. I was careful to speak respectfully. I come from an Indian Administrative Service (IAS) family, and had dealt with IAS officers before. I knew that you can't afford to antagonize them because they wield enormous power.

Datta-Ghosh cut me off. 'The money you are investing is peanuts,' she said curtly. 'India is not a banana republic, and we can take care of our own problems.' A meeting between the prime minister and

Bill Gates that the foundation had asked for had not yet been cleared, as protocol required, by the health ministry and soon the headlines were about the cold shoulder that the government was giving to the foundation.[5]

We had underestimated the amount of jingoism, as also the extent of sheer denial about HIV/AIDS, in the government. But, fortunately, wiser counsels prevailed, and Bill and I were ushered into Prime Minister Atal Bihari Vajpayee's wood-panelled office as scheduled, two days later. The prime minister was gracious. 'I believe you have been going around spreading alarm,' he chuckled. Expressing his belief in the foundation's commitment to help India fight AIDS, he said, 'I assure you of every support my government can give you in your programme.' They were reassuring words.

Two liveried butlers arrived, each bearing a vast tray of a variety of Indian sweetmeats and western cake and pastries, which were offered first to Bill. As Bill declined, the prime minister reached over and took a piece of cake from the tray. He chewed slowly, swallowed, and turned to Bill, saying, 'I assure you they are quite safe!' The meeting ended with laughter.

Bill told the press massed outside the prime minister's house that he was gratified by the prime minister's warmth and assurance of support from the Government of India. The storm seemed to have blown over. But for me, there was still plenty of rough weather to follow.

~

Everything had gone well so far. Bill Gates had come and gone and set things up very nicely. Everybody wanted to be my friend. The press loved me. I was drinking it all in. There was the poignancy of leaving McKinsey, the rounds of farewell parties, the warmth of welcome from the foundation, the excitement of the grant announcement, and the heady anticipation of what lay ahead. I had a spring in my step.

It didn't last. My first six months with the Gates Foundation, the period from December 2002 through May 2003,[6] were surprisingly trying, a series of rude shocks, from unanticipated directions.

My first shock came from, of all places, the foundation. Soon after Bill's departure I asked Helene Gayle how big a team I should build, with what kind of people, and her response had me reeling. 'Well, we haven't budgeted for any kind of team. We figured your job was to make a lot of grants with the money and oversee the implementation.' Helene must have noticed that I was almost choking, because she added, 'I don't think there would be any harm if you hired a secretary and took a small office.'

It suddenly hit me that despite all my talk about 'local presence' and a 'foundation team on the ground', they had never really absorbed what I meant. When I look back at this now, I can appreciate that it was the foundation's first office outside of Seattle, and they just didn't understand how things worked in India. At that time, I was angry and bitter. Here I was, I felt, talked out of a director position at McKinsey, taking an enormous pay cut, ostensibly to stop HIV in India – and I was expected to do it without a team! I felt frustrated, and some self-pity. There was no going back to McKinsey, and it seemed to me there was no way to go forward.

I am not very patient and find it difficult at times like this to hide my feelings. I drew a deep breath and told Helene that the task was impossible, and that I needed a team of at least fifteen people. Helene said, 'I understand what you are saying, and I'm on your side, but let's do it the right way. Let's commission a strategy exercise.' I reminded Helene with a sniff that I had spent a career building competitive strategies for the world's smartest companies. I had a good idea of how to go about things, and I didn't need a bunch of 'experts' from the health sector telling me what to do. I'd totally lost it by now.

'Trust me on this,' said Helene. 'The foundation is not going to give you resources just because you ask. They are very clear about not getting directly involved in implementation. They will, though, buy into the recommendations of a report done by some of the world's best experts. I'm sure one of their recommendations will be that you should be given the leeway to build a team.'

I insisted that the exercise be completed within six weeks because I wanted to get to work quickly. Helene assembled a team led by Tony Bondurant, a respected HIV consultant specializing in programme management. There were five other members, each an expert in a different functional area. In the end, we had a decent-looking report that we presented to the foundation. We had estimated that we needed much more money if we were to run Avahan at the scale needed. We asked for another hundred million dollars and a team of six to start. Patty Stonesifer asked some sharp questions and, over the course of the meeting at the foundation's headquarters in Seattle, we got the needed sanctions. Helene is too decent a person to ever say 'I told you so', and she just smiled.

Even as I tussled for resources I received another unpleasant surprise, this time from the other players involved in the fight against HIV.

~

Waiters circulated, offering exotic canapes and an assortment of fine wines. Two hundred formally attired guests milled around. It was a dinner party on World AIDS Day, 2 December 2002. Here, NGO heads sucked up to the head of NACO; there, mediapeople cosied up to celebrities, discussing everything but the HIV epidemic. I came in feeling like an outsider, but suddenly I was one of the much sought-after people in the room. After all, they thought I had two hundred million dollars in my back pocket.

Except for one person. A tiny woman with a short haircut and an Australian twang came up to me. She thrust out her hand, gave me a firm handshake, and said, 'Hi Ashok, can I have a word with you?' She suggested we move to a far corner and introduced herself as the India head of a respected international NGO, working on HIV/AIDS.

The lady had a pale complexion that was steadily turning red. She got straight to the point: 'I have one question – what the hell do you know about HIV?' I was taken aback, and said something lame like 'Not much actually, but I'm learning every day'. She leaned forward and hissed: 'I'll tell you something, mate – it's not that easy. Some of us have spent a lifetime learning the ropes. This isn't some smarty McKinsey exercise.'

I learnt later that the foundation had consulted with experts around the world for advice on how to design its campaign against AIDS in India. Having provided their inputs, many NGOs would have hoped to be the agency chosen to receive the implementation grant. This NGO had apparently been a front runner for the much envied position of contractor – at least till the foundation decided at the very last minute to put me in charge. I muttered something about needing to work together, valuing her counsel and her guidance, and so on. She turned on her heel and walked off.

I took no offence, because I could well understand her anger. She was to become a good friend and we worked closely in the years that followed. She passed away prematurely some years later, literally in the line of duty, working late at night on what was by then our very real partnership.

~

I was to get another shock, this time because I had not done my homework. According to NACO estimates, in 2003 there were about five million people living with HIV in India. The world viewed India's epidemic with some alarm, with fears that it could go the way of countries like Botswana and South Africa, where in 2003 HIV affected over 37.3 and 21.5 per cent of the adult population respectively.[7]

It dawned on me that I was there to lead the creation of a programme to help stop all that. I began to consult with international experts, and they all told me that HIV prevention was one of the most difficult of public health problems. There were few examples of prevention done on a large scale. The countries cited as success stories – Thailand, Uganda, and Brazil – were much smaller than India, and far less complex. I heard that the experts were saying: 'The Gates Foundation has good intentions, but this is one dumb investment. How are they going to scale this up, and that too led by a person with no experience with HIV?'

~

Meanwhile, my teething problems with the foundation were not yet over. I was told that legal, finance, and human resources would have to figure out how much to pay us, and how to do it. I was told this process 'could take a few months, definitely not before the last quarter'. The implication was that I hold off recruiting till then. I gritted my teeth. 'Just go ahead,' I said, 'but I'd appreciate it if you could do this as fast as possible.'

I had no intention of sitting around waiting for the foundation to figure out how they would pay me. So I set about building a team who would not get paid for the time being. The first recruit was my long-suffering assistant Debbie Seymour, who decided to leave McKinsey to join me. She was part of the 'you can hire an assistant' deal, so it was possible for me to pay Debbie from the outset.

Alkesh Wadhwani was a highly regarded manager at McKinsey, who had told me he wanted to join up, soon after I announced my departure. At that time I had no idea what I could pay him, or even if I could ever pay him. Alkesh has an uncanny way of getting to core issues quickly. 'I've been desperate to do something like this for a long time. Take me on, and pay me whatever you can, whenever you can – and I don't care if it ends up being zero.' How could I say no to that?

I recruited another smart young person from McKinsey in New York, Aparajita Ramakrishnan, who also felt the call. We agreed that I would pay her two thousand dollars a month from my own pocket, and that she would pay me back when her own salary was eventually worked out. We also had Manisha Bharti, who somehow was able to join us for three months as a consultant paid for by UNAIDS. She had been working in HIV/AIDS and knew the theory of prevention. Manisha was a great asset in those early days.

I was approached by three young, super-bright analysts from McKinsey, and the Firm generously said they would pay their salaries. They were a bonus, in that they fell outside of the sanctioned staff of six. Shivanshu Gupta, Amit Soni, and Nishant Sharma stayed a year before going on to Ivy League business schools in the United States. They were smart, personable, and tireless, and their role was to gather data through field interviews. They each had a wicked sense of humour which always kept things lively.

It never struck me then, but must have struck many people, that six of the seven people on my starting team were from McKinsey. It was not that I felt there wasn't talent elsewhere. It was just me reaching out instinctively to a place I knew. In fact, none of my recruits after that were from the Firm.

Now I had a team – and so what if most were not getting paid by the foundation, and only one knew anything about HIV? We began work from two rooms in a small business centre in Nehru Place. It was nothing fancy, something like a warm shack, but it was an office of our own. Everyone started getting paid six months later, and I began recruiting in earnest.

~

Amid all these trials there were surreal moments, often even hilarious, as we set about discovering the world of HIV. One such was my first encounter with the female condom.

I was in a transition period between McKinsey and the foundation in early 2003. The Firm had let me keep my office, till such time as I set up my own workplace. It often felt unreal as I returned from field trips to the grey-suit-white-shirt-dark-tie environment of the Firm, for a day or so every week. There were a lot of people wanting to see me in those days. I would get calls all the time from NGOs that wanted to implement parts of the Avahan programme or had products they felt should be delivered on a massive scale.

One such product was the female condom. The FC, as it is called, had been around since the 1980s. It was made of polyurethane, a thin, loose-fitting sheath with a ring at each end. The advantage of the FC was that the woman had more control – she could wear it without the man knowing, and so it was very popular with sex workers. Unlike the regular latex condom, it could transmit heat, and thereby felt closer to unprotected sex. It came in different sizes and was also popular with those who favoured anal sex. The problem was its prohibitive cost.

I had never heard of the FC, but by then I'd already seen a lot of things I'd never imagined. I was on a learning curve, so when Jennifer Grass asked for an appointment to tell me about the FC, I readily agreed. Jennifer was the head of an international NGO that specialized in the FC. She walked into the small meeting room with an ordinary-looking briefcase in her hand. Jennifer was young, and really passionate about her product. I called the office boy for two cups of tea and began to listen intently. She showed me brochures and unwrapped a packet of the condoms for me to examine. The product looked strange, and I couldn't quite understand how it worked, and I was full of questions.

'Would you like to see how it works? You can insert it yourself,' Jennifer said. The world of HIV prevention is very direct, and sometimes raw for the uninitiated. I was still getting used to it, and I blushed faintly, confused about what she had in mind. Jumping up, she opened the briefcase to reveal a convincing mannequin, a female torso, with the legs cut off just above the knees. Due north from there was the pelvic area with a small tuft of pubic hair, a vulva – all the fixings. Going further north, the mannequin had pert breasts and a fashionable short crop of hair.

I still didn't know what to do, so Jennifer asked me to take two fingers, push them into the FC, and then simply insert the condom into the mannequin's vagina. She showed me how to do it and placed my fingers, sheathed by the condom, against the vulva. 'Now just push it in, slowly, gently.' I got it in on my second attempt and was very pleased with myself. I tried it a few times.

I was bending by the mannequin, when there was a knock on the door, and Ram, the office boy, walked in with two cups of steaming tea and some cookies. His jaw dropped at the sight of me with my fingers inside what looked like a life-size doll. Ram maintained his professional dignity, set the tray down, and asked if there was anything else I needed. He left, closing the door gently behind him.

We both burst out laughing.

~

When I stepped out of McKinsey, I was brimming with confidence. I thought the task ahead was like any other client assignment, though perhaps a little more challenging. I was nervous in a healthy way, and never doubted that we'd figure it out. Now, a few weeks in, I felt a frisson of concern.

We were the lead player in the battle against HIV, amid fears about a galloping epidemic, a government in denial, attempting something that had not been done before, without a clear model. I did not have a real team, and it seemed as though the foundation and I were on different wavelengths. We were being viewed by the government with suspicion, and by many NGOs with derision. I was starting to find out that many sex workers had bigger priorities than HIV prevention, that my suppositions about solutions were naive, and that HIV prevention with very large numbers of highly at-risk people had never worked anywhere in the world. I realized I had not done even the basic homework required before taking on such a huge challenge. I was getting that sensation that every McKinsey person dreads – the feeling of being exposed.

Instinctively, I knew that the only way for us to move forward was to go deep into the field. It was to be a transformational process, which took me, personally, from despair to hope.

3

Into the Shadowlands

Following from that first field trip to Vizag, I got into a steady rhythm of weekly travel. Our circuit was six states – Maharashtra, Andhra Pradesh, Karnataka, Tamil Nadu, Manipur, and Nagaland – and the regions of highest HIV prevalence within each. These were sometimes journeys to places of enchanting beauty and the vilest squalor. One week with injecting drug users on the border with Myanmar, the other at the biggest truck stop in Asia, on the outskirts of Delhi; one week with chanting Devadasis in Belgaum or tamasha girls near Sangli, the next with transgenders in the dark recesses of Cubbon Park, Bangalore; tea in the huge Budhwar Peth brothel in Pune, and then on to meet with Kalavanthula women, traditional courtesans[1] on the banks of the magnificent Godavari river in Andhra Pradesh. We went to Punjab and Rajasthan, northern states where HIV was reported to be low. There were also learning trips to countries where HIV was spreading its tentacles – Cambodia, Thailand, Indonesia, and Bangladesh.

I journeyed to places where commercial sex or risky behaviour was abundant, and the HIV virus moved, silent and untrammelled, along its deadly pathways. I saw the same scenes being repeated in different guises everywhere. I came back from these early field trips sometimes badly shaken. There was a wretchedness of human circumstances I had never seen before: the endless manifestations of sex work, the hopelessness of drug injectors, the loneliness of those dying of AIDS, and the brutal personal introductions to what the term public health really meant. But as I continued my field engagement, I also started to appreciate the courage and strength of the communities that lived in these circumstances.

~

Returning from a grinding field trip, I was unwinding one Saturday evening at the home of a good friend from my college days. When I decided to join the Gates Foundation, my friends had congratulated me. They were supportive of my new work on what seemed a noble social cause. But as time passed, I sensed that no one really knew, or really wanted to know, what I did. It was somewhere far away, a problem that didn't affect the kind of people they knew, and therefore was not part of their daily concerns.

At dinner that evening my friend said, 'So Choki [my nickname], what do you really see on these field trips? Isn't this AIDS thing exaggerated? Why can't these sex workers insist on condoms? They should be thrown in jail if they don't. I believe they do that in Thailand.'

I proceeded to explain the 'AIDS thing' and why condom use was sometimes so difficult for a sex worker to negotiate. I had been so immersed in this world of late that it didn't feel odd to share a story from a recent field trip at a dinner party. After all, it was part of my daily experience now. I told of a young mother I had met at a community centre in Medak, a small town some two hours north of Hyderabad, once famous because Indira Gandhi chose it as her parliamentary constituency. The girl, about eighteen years old, had two children with her – one in her lap, a girl about a year old, the other a boy of two. Both children were clean and well scrubbed. Something struck me about this child with children, perhaps her aura of innocence, or her quiet beauty. She didn't seem like a sex worker and I asked her if she would tell me about herself.

The girl was shy, and obviously unused to being asked questions. When she spoke, her words came out haltingly, and the NGO translator was visibly struggling. 'My name is Kamla. I was married when I was fifteen, and three years later I had two children. My husband left me for another woman, and I took up sex work because there was no other way to take care of my children. I practise on the street and charge thirty rupees for an encounter. On a regular day I make a hundred rupees. If I am lucky it can even be two hundred.'

A journalist from Agence France-Press (AFP) was writing a story about us, and we were travelling together throughout this week in the field, together with his photographer. 'What is the most difficult situation you have faced in your life?' he interjected, wanting to cut to the chase. I cringed at his insensitivity, but the question had been asked.

For a long time, there was no response. Finally, the girl spoke in a voice that could barely be heard. 'It was just last week, sir. It is very difficult to do sex work when you must take two babies with you everywhere. I met a man at the city bus stand. He gave me twenty rupees for an autorickshaw and asked me to meet him two hours later in a deserted area on the outskirts of the city.

'When I reached, it was dusk. I cannot have sex in front of my children, so I usually find a sheltered spot to leave them and go behind the bushes with my customer – after all, it takes only a few minutes. I went to the meeting place which was close by, and suddenly I saw five men, one was the man who had given me twenty rupees. Empty bottles were everywhere, darkness was coming, and I immediately thought of my children. I turned to run, but one of the men caught me by the hair. They took turns beating and raping me, and I was terrified for my children. Half an hour went by in this way, what if my children had been eaten by dogs, or if my toddler had wandered away?

'I begged the men to stop for just a few minutes, so I could go and bring my children, but there was no stopping them, they went on and on, and I wept for my children. Though they tortured me, all the pain I felt was the thought that I would never see my children again. After more than two hours the men threw me away. I staggered to the spot where I had left my children, they were sleeping peacefully in each other's arms. I had no money but I somehow managed to get back to Medak.' The reporter put away his pad, and the photographer stopped clicking.

I looked up from my story. The room was quiet; all conversation had stopped. People cleared their throats uneasily. The hostess announced dinner. The next day my friend called: 'Choki, that was a simply awful story you told about the woman and her kids. It got a lot of people upset. Can you just cut out your field stories next time?' I readily agreed. A vast gulf separated people with HIV from those with any other health condition. After that I stopped discussing my work in casual conversation.

~

There were many myths and misconceptions about sex work in India. Many people believed that in India it is on a smaller, less significant scale than in other parts of Asia. 'Ours is a moral society,' a leading politician told me. 'We don't have much prostitution in India, and the risk of HIV spreading that way is so much exaggerated. Why doesn't your foundation spend its good money on something else?' He proceeded to describe the benefits that would accrue if our funds were invested in the development of his constituency.

I cited figures that showed that the extent of sex work in India was consistent with global norms – about five women in every thousand according to one survey.[2] This got the politician flustered. 'Even if there are prostitutes, very few men go to them. We are faithful to our loved ones . . . chee chee chee . . .' he said, conveying revulsion. 'And even if a few bad men go to sex workers,' he blustered, 'AIDS will not spread because of that. Men and women don't have sex outside marriage in our country. Our women are sati savitris. In the villages a woman will not even look at a man who is not her husband or close relative.'

The politician had his basic epidemiology right. HIV requires concurrent sexual relationships – sex with someone who is not your

spouse or regular partner – to spread into the general population. This
was lower in India, acting as a brake. But I enjoyed throwing some more
data at him, indicating that in 2001 almost 10 per cent of Indian men
and 2 per cent of Indian women had sex with a 'non-regular partner'
every year. I mentioned that some states seemed to be more prolific in
this respect. Subsequent government data showed that as many as 26
per cent of men and 9 per cent[3] of women in rural Andhra Pradesh
had concurrent relationships, well over the urban norm.

In other words, our preliminary data showed that sex work and
sexual relationships in India were no different from those in other
societies, and people had the same vulnerabilities. Indian women
practised sex work as much as women elsewhere; Indian men went
to sex workers as much as men in other countries did; and men and
women had sex quite often with people other than their spouses. But
everywhere we encountered reactions like the politician's: not in *our*
country.

The real problem was that Indians generally were unwilling to
face up to issues about sex and sexuality, and so stigma, apathy, and
denial over HIV were widespread. It was there among politicians,
policymakers, media, the public at large – and even my friends. It was
one of the most disheartening aspects of my new job, when I got
started.

~

Some months earlier, sitting with nineteen other sex workers on the
floor of a safe house in Vizag, Rajamma had told me (see chapter 1)
why I couldn't solve her problems, leave alone those of all the women
in that room. It was my first lesson in the meaning of public health –
you can't set out to save every life individually. An old-timer in public
health had told me it was unethical to get engaged in individual life-
saving, when your mission was to serve the community. Two heart-
breaking encounters in Manipur again drove home to me what public
health really meant.

Manipur is one of India's most beautiful and neglected states. Ravaged by insurgency and desperately poor, it is a sad, forgotten place. Among Manipur's tragedies was a severe HIV epidemic that was a consequence of widespread injecting drug use. HIV and drugs were destroying the social fabric.

On my first trip to Imphal, the capital of Manipur, in 2003, late one evening I visited a care centre for HIV positive people. In the flickering light, emaciated bodies lay on metal beds, attached to tubes. Some searched our faces desperately for the fleeting soft touch of eye contact. I stopped beside a young man who seemed to have no life in him and took his hand, which was surprisingly warm.

'Antheim has very low CD4 count, barely 200.[4] He will not live long unless we start giving him ART.' The doctor was referring to antiretroviral treatment, the new life-extending treatment, not yet available through the government. It was expensive and, even if accessible, was out of the reach of the very poor and marginalized. 'ART will cost about three thousand rupees a month,' the doctor said, 'and Antheim needs at least six months of treatment to stabilize, and then regular monitoring after that. We can make it available, but his family can't afford it. We can treat very few people here. We give them care and nutrition and send them home, often to die.'

I felt a chill as I released Antheim's hand. In my wallet, I had enough loose notes to keep him alive for several months. I wanted to thrust the money at the doctor and get away, but I paused and moved on, the message about public health, not private charity, ringing in my ears. That night, I was haunted by the image of the dying young man, the same age as my younger son. Since my first conversation with the sex workers in Vizag, I had encountered many people who desperately needed help. I told myself that offering money on the spot was simply not a solution. I convinced myself there was no end to it, I simply could not thrust money into the hands of every desperate person I met. But the look in Antheim's eyes as I walked away simply broke my heart. I decided to return to the hospital the next day and offer the money.

But the next day, in broad daylight and back to rational logic, I did not go back. We departed in a hurry, scrambling to get in the car. I wept bitterly in my room that night. I wondered if I was also part of the huge indifference that surrounded HIV, but just with a better excuse. The memory of that dark room, the flickering light, the look in the boy's eyes as he met mine, it sometimes comes back to me and can still bring tears to my eyes. I tell myself Antheim is still alive, and he is healthy. But I have no way of knowing if that's true.

~

Today, through ART, a person with HIV can live a full lifespan. In 2003, ART had just made an entry into India, and contracting HIV was a virtual death sentence.[5] As the HIV viral load climbed it would destroy the CD4 cells that acted as the body's immune system and the person would enter by stages into full-blown AIDS. He would waste away and die an agonizing death. The entire cycle could take eight to ten years to play out.

Some months before our first trip to Manipur, we visited Tambaram Hospital in Chennai. It was then the largest AIDS hospital in Asia, and the only major HIV care centre in India. Tambaram sprawls over 250 acres in the green hills of Pachamalai near the Chennai International Airport. Established in 1928, Tambaram Hospital had been functioning purely as a tuberculosis sanatorium till the early 1990s. Then it started taking in HIV patients as well, as those numbers began to grow. When we visited, Tambaram was seeing over 150 outpatients a day from across India. There were only three hundred beds, however, so inpatient treatment was constrained.

We were moved to see the valiant attempts by the doctors and nurses at Tambaram to provide some level of care. HIV treatment was not easily available at that time, and the patients only received a nutritious diet and traditional Siddha medicine, which barely had a palliative effect. As we walked through the AIDS wards, it was hard to keep my composure at the sight of the helpless, especially the children. Some struggled to sit up in their beds to offer a namaste, for some form of contact with another human being. Perhaps they were thinking that the fancy people from outside had a cure they could hand out.

We walked to one of the women's wards and the contrast was striking. There was a small crowd outside the men's wards – mothers, wives, and children who had accompanied the patient and were all living outside the hospital with makeshift arrangements. The area outside the women's wards, however, was almost empty. No one had come with them. There was a much higher level of stigma towards women with HIV.

'We release the patients usually after two weeks, after treating their superficial infections,' said an overworked young doctor. 'Many try to come back soon after, under an assumed name. They have nowhere to go, and here they are looked after. Sometimes their families have rejected them. Above all, here they feel cared for.'

The complete inadequacy of treatment was to strike me many times during subsequent field trips. The question we were asked over and over was why we weren't giving money for care and treatment. The answer we always gave was that prevention was even more important, because a single case prevented multiple infections. It saved more lives, from a public health viewpoint. Sometimes, confronted with the sight of a dying HIV positive person, it seemed an inadequate logic.

~

In Imphal, on a later trip, the choice confronted me again. Returning to Manipur's capital after a day in the interior, I wanted only to stagger into my hotel room, put a double lock on my door, and sleep.

'Sir, if you would spare just twenty minutes, we want you to visit the General Hospital,' our NGO host said. Bone tired, I said I simply could not because we had finished our day's itinerary. Also, I would not be able to do anything through Avahan to respond to the needs of people in the hospital because our focus was on prevention, not treatment. 'Please sir,' said the host, 'it's a baby, hardly two years old, we just want you to see.'

The Imphal General Hospital was spilling over with patients, in the corridors and in the stairwell. Sinking people, connected to plastic bags held up by hollow-eyed family, lay everywhere. I climbed up the two flights to the paediatric ward, experiencing a mounting sense of dread with every step. There I had my first sight of Danny, howling his lungs out and punching the back of the laughing nurse who held him. Danny's hair, and even his skin, seemed orange from infection. I had never seen a baby like this. 'Don't worry, sir,' the doctor said, seeing my alarm. 'The little fellow is totally fine, he is receiving treatment, and responding very well. He just has a few scabs that are healing very nicely. In fact, he is ready to go home.'

'And where is his home, and where will he go now?' I asked, as I took a now calmer Danny into my arms. 'Well, that's the problem,' the doctor sighed, and he told me Danny's story.

Danny lived with his paternal grandparents in a tiny shack on the outskirts of Imphal. His father had been an injecting drug user who died in his early twenties. Danny's mother followed two years later. This is a typical pattern: the injecting drug user contracts HIV from shared needles, passes it on to his wife, and they both die in quick succession. Danny had received the virus in his mother's womb, and was now left in the care of his aged grandparents.

One morning his grandparents called the local NGO and asked that they take Danny away. 'We found Danny in the courtyard outside his house,' someone from the NGO told the doctor. 'His grandparents had put him out there, a small glass of black tea in his hands. They thought he had a devil inside him, which spread HIV to anyone who touched him. They didn't come out when we took the baby away. We brought him to the General Hospital, where they found that his CD4 was very low. We were able to get him on treatment, and he has made a dramatic recovery. In fact, he is perfectly healthy now.'

Danny had fallen into a peaceful sleep as the nurse rocked him. 'The real problem begins now,' said the doctor. 'You can't really blame his grandparents. They believe the baby is possessed and will kill everyone around him. And we can't send him home, because he no longer has a home. There are no shelters we can send him to, certainly not one where we can find the treatment he needs. And the NGO must get back to its main work, which is not about caring for AIDS orphans. Do you think you can help?'

That night I called my friend Anjali Gopalan, who runs the Naz Foundation, a home for HIV positive orphans in New Delhi. Anjali has a tough exterior, but she is an angel in disguise. I stammered about Danny's situation, how I had a flight to catch the next day, and what was I to do? 'So, what's the problem?' Anjali said immediately. 'Just bring him over.'

I used to visit NAZ, mainly to get a peek at Danny, for some years after that, sometimes with a cake on my birthday. I called Anjali in 2017 for this book, and of course asked straight away about Danny. She said, 'Ashok, I'll tell you something amazing that's happened since you last saw him. He was turning into a bit of a problem child, and we were really worried about him. From the beginning, other children teased him because he looked "Chinese", and he became withdrawn, and was also getting into fights. Then he took to athletics – the high jump and the long jump – and he has broken a lot of records. His coach now says the boy is too good, and he can't give him the more advanced training that he needs. He says Danny can represent India at the Olympics one day! He has recommended where we should send him.'

I decided to go and see Danny. I was taken aback to see a strapping, good-looking, soft-spoken young man of sixteen. He had the kind of sharp hairstyle that youngsters tend to favour these days. He told me he was into coaching younger children.

Danny's story was illustrative of the confounding depths of stigma associated with HIV in India. Manipur is a state which has a centuries-old tradition of family, which obliged people to welcome even an enemy who entered their village as an honoured guest and treat him as part of the family. But this virus had led grandparents to cast out their own grandchild. What would it do eventually to Manipuri society? Could anyone really hope to defeat such a powerful virus?

~

A field trip we made in August 2003 was different. It was to a slum outside Chandigarh, 250 kilometres north of Delhi. We wanted to get a sense of the urban slum environment as a setting for HIV. But the more specific reason was to get a sense of Punjab as a place where injecting drug use – associated so far only with the North-East – was said to be growing. If that were to happen in Punjab, it could spill over into Delhi and beyond, a frightening prospect.[6] There was no reliable data on drug use outside of the North-East.

Chandigarh, with a population of about one million in 2003, is a comparatively new city, created as the capital of two states, Punjab and Haryana, in 1966. It is a well-planned city, designed by the famous architect Le Corbusier, nestling in the foothills of the Himalaya. After meeting with the Punjab State AIDS Control Society (SACS), we set out with one of their senior staff to a large urban slum with a population of over three thousand people. The slum fell within the city limits but was located close to its outskirts.

The slum was surrounded by small hills of rotting garbage, where pigs and stray dogs rummaged. It consisted of about five hundred houses of varying sizes. Most were hovels, but there were also a few dwellings where the better-off lived. A shiny motorcycle parked outside or a TV dish antenna marked out such houses and reflected their elevated status. A narrow pathway ran along the centre of the slum. Small shops were sprinkled about the main pathway, many adorned with strings of the junk food packets that were becoming ubiquitous all over India.

Atmaram, widely known as 'chacha' (uncle), was the leader of the slum. Wiry, big-moustached, and clad in checked dhoti and faded T-shirt, he gave us a broad smile, revealing rust-red teeth and a crimson tongue, evidence of an addiction to chewing tambaku-paan. Chacha ran the slum through a draconian system of rules that were very clearly understood by all. He maintained strict discipline in terms of adherence to these rules, swiftly dispensing reward or punishment, as warranted.

There was no value judgement attached to Atmaram's system of justice. As he showed us around, he pointed out the sex work section. He told us that alcohol was widely consumed, mainly country liquor. Drugs were freely available, including heroin ('smack') which was gaining in popularity. His outlook was not to stop anything, but to take his cut, offer his protection, and see that nothing got out of control. His main role was to ensure that the entire slum population functioned as a vote bank for a particular political party.

Atmaram said, 'This place needs strong discipline. You have no idea what goes on. Just the other day I found someone with a dog in this field. I broke both his legs. Kids drive up here from the city in their swanky cars, from rich families. They get the drugs here and shoot up right away, don't even bother to hide . . .' As he spoke, he noticed scum water spilling over from an open gutter. He reached for a broom and cleaned up the blockage himself, and the water flowed again.

A small group had gathered around, keeping a safe distance from Atmaram, to gawk at the 'doctors' from the city. One of them stood out. He was a lanky Sikh, perhaps thirty-five, with henna-red hair and beard, loose turban aslant, and a distinctly demented look, though in an amiable way. He swayed gently, and looked at first as though he was leering, but I realized he was only attempting an ingratiating smile. Atmaram called out to him: 'You! Come here, tell the doctor sahibs what goes on.'

The sardar shuffled over, warily scratching his crotch. He spoke in a very rough Punjabi that we had a tough time following. He was speaking of the slum, and about his experiences in jail. At the word 'jail' the government officer who had accompanied us woke up: 'Did you say jail, Sardarji? How long were you in?'

'A sentence of fourteen years, rigorous,' the sardar replied, with a touch of pride in his voice.

'Fourteen years!' exclaimed the government officer. 'That's a lot. You must have been in for murder then?'

'Damn right it was murder,' said the sardar, now swelling with pride. 'The madarchod – motherfucker – tried to take my land. Naturally, I took a gun and blew him to pieces.' He said this as though it was the right and proper thing to do. 'My jail experience was good,' he went on to say. 'I ran drugs for the first five years. Started with simple things like Calmpose and worked my way to smack and even morphine. I was let off in ten years for good behaviour.' There was a trace of wistfulness in his recounting of his jail days.

The afternoon was beginning to feel distinctly unreal. 'You should interview some of our local doctors,' Atmaram said. I knew he meant unqualified doctors – quacks. The first such person was intimidated to meet 'doctors' from Delhi and assured us he would never treat STIs because he knew his limitations, and that he would always refer such cases. The second was a Bengali, who seemed embarrassed – they are a people who aspire to intellectual pursuits – that he had been reduced to practising medicine in this manner, so far away from home. The third was a woman, which was unusual in this role. Interestingly, the sex workers preferred to bypass her and go to her male competitors. All three provided reliable and discreet services, within the limits of their knowledge. There was no government medical facility inside the slum, no school that we could see, because these were 'unauthorized' colonies, falling outside the municipality's jurisdiction.

This slum was a sad ecosystem of drugs, alcohol, and sex work. The garbage outside and the rot inside gave me a sense of a place in decay, devoid of hope, sliding down. As we went to our car, a little stray dog ran up from the garbage heap, eagerly wagging his tail. He was lovely to look at – till I saw something that made my stomach turn. One side of the top of his head had been eaten away, and I could see deep inside. He wagged his tail at us as we drove away, seemingly oblivious to his condition.

~

In Malad, a predominantly Muslim area of Mumbai, I walked through the slums where over three thousand of Mumbai's bar girls lived. Everywhere, there was squalor – open sewers, piles of rotting garbage, swarms of flies. People did not linger, they hurried, as though to escape the decay.

We climbed up a steep, almost ladder-like, staircase and stepped into a room about ten feet by fifteen feet, where ten women lived. Six of them sat on a worn-out, stained mattress on the floor. A ceiling fan slowly churned the humid air. There were two wall lights, of which one had died. The other glowed dimly, and at times threatened to go out, and the room would be in near darkness. All of a sudden, the bulb would flare up, briefly bathe the room with stronger light, then fade back to the dim glow which seemed to be its normal state.

The women had been assembled to meet us by the NGO that we were funding to work with bar girls in Mumbai. The women wore no mascara or the bright lipstick that they used during their working hours. Most were in their early twenties, but now at home they looked haggard, with hollow eyes and sallow, wrinkled skin. They told me they each paid the landlord a hundred rupees a day. This was an exorbitant rate for a hovel, but clearly the girls had no other recourse. Some paid much more, depending on how desperate their circumstances were. Realizing that we were depriving the girls of the few hours of rest that they got between shifts, we terminated the discussion and stepped back on to the street.

There were separate sections in the slum for women from different states, such as Rajasthan, Uttar Pradesh, and West Bengal. The fate of these women, particularly the few who were immigrants from Bangladesh, was pathetic. Several of them had come with families and the bar girl's earnings would support her 'husband', children, and sometimes even her parents. They worked in bars some distance away from the slums where they lived, and would return by about four each morning, totally exhausted, often inebriated. They were in no condition then to take care of their children, and the child might be given some narcotic so that the mother could sleep till about two in the afternoon.

By four, the bar girl would leave for work. If she had no family, she sometimes had no alternative but to lock her child in the room and leave the key with a neighbour. She might also entrust the child to her 'husband', when he was there, and he usually took about two hundred rupees every day of her earnings. The husbands spent the afternoons with their friends, idling away playing carom or cards. A smaller group, who fancied that they were poets – after all, they were Bengali – would indulge in sher-shayari, the reciting of couplets that they had composed. Meanwhile, the bar girl reaches her establishment. She puts on her make-up, paints her lips, pulls on her tight skirt and top, and steps into the bar, looking young and pretty in the dim light.

There were several categories of bars. In the 'disco bar' the customer would negotiate an encounter with the bar girl, and the two would retire for a short time to the sex-rooms available on the first level of the premises. The girls told me they would see seven to ten clients every day. There were also the 'dance bars' where the proprietor would not allow sex on the premises, and the girls might agree to meet customers, but only after their shift. Then there were the 'silent bars' that were very dark, because the girls serviced customers with a hand job or oral sex on the spot. Penetrative sex was not allowed. The bar girls were known as 'service girls' if they were open to having sex or as 'dance girls', whose job was to chat with the customers and ply them with drinks. The bar owner had a system through which he got a straight 50 per cent commission on all sex transactions.

Talking to the NGO worker Asha, I learnt how tough and stressful the life of a bar girl was. She told me: 'Some of the girls have slash marks on their wrists. One I saw recently had as many as twenty.' I wondered whether she had been slashed or whether the wounds were self-inflicted. Ashamed, I did not ask. Asha said, 'At twenty-five they look old and wizened, and many may not be alive ten years later.'

The bar girl business is lucrative, and there was a Bar-Owners Association that had three factions. Each was controlled by a leader, one of whom was a woman. Many of the leaders run registered NGOs, well regarded for the charitable work they do. One of them pulled out an album with photographs that showed him receiving high awards. One, taken a few years back, took me by surprise because in it he was receiving a trophy of some sort from my father, who then happened to be the Governor of Maharashtra![7]

The real power, however, lay behind the curtain. The Mumbai underworld was said to be involved. It was widely known that one of the most powerful politicians in the state owned three dance bars. A former police commissioner's son owned one of the largest in the city. The trip was a revelation. I'd assumed that bar girls would be much better off than the regular female sex workers, because of the veneer of glamour and the air-conditioned settings. Yet the situation of these girls, completely disempowered, unable to demand condom use from clients, said otherwise. A wave of sadness overcame me as I left Malad that evening for Delhi.

~

Sex work at the bottom of the pyramid is not a pretty thing. It is a war for survival. The people I met often lived in desperate situations. In the brothels, some women had been trafficked into the profession as children, even sold by their own parents. In homes, women were victims of domestic violence and neglect, and, on the streets, they faced violence from the police and goons. Their children had no safe place, except perhaps under their mother's bed when she was with a client. She was unable to secure a government ration card for subsidized rice and wheat, or easily gain admittance into the government hospital because of the stigma of her profession. They had no savings, tending to burn up the occasional windfall gain from a generous client on impromptu partying. Their lives were a litany of problems big and small.

Initially I would try to engage the women in a discussion about HIV and warn them of the dangers of unprotected sex. But I soon realized they had far more serious issues on their mind than HIV. Some of the women tried to explain. First there was Rajamma, whom I had met in Vizag. A year later Theny, twenty-five, a street-based sex worker, explained the same thing to me through a personal story. I met her in Dharmapuri, a small town in western Tamil Nadu.

'Sir, you are telling me that I must use condoms. But sex work is my trade. I can teach you some things you don't know about condoms.' Her friends joined in her laughter. But then her expression turned serious. 'Do you think I don't want to use condoms? This happened just last week. My child was running a high fever, he needed medicine, some nourishing food. I needed four hundred rupees right away. The client did not want to use a condom, he was drunk. I said, "Sir, let's use the condom. Who knows, I may have HIV, and you have a wife at home after all." Without warning, he slapped me hard, threw five hundred rupees on the bed, and shouted, "Paccha thevudia! [Fucking whore!] Come on, spread your legs." So, what should I have done? Could I just follow your advice and use the condom? You are telling me that if I get HIV I will die in ten years' time. But sir, ten years is a lifetime for me. I have other more serious things to worry about now.'

'And what are these things?' I asked, with a sinking feeling.

'Find a boarding school for our kids. Or give us a life free from violence,' said Theny.

Afterwards, I was to look back at this conversation and understand that hidden in her words was the solution to the problem of scaling up HIV prevention in India.

~

At McKinsey I often told clients how India worked. I could talk about the political environment which was then in a state of flux, draw out the implications for industry, and highlight for them the opportunities and the threats in an India striding boldly into the new millennium.

What I didn't talk about was poverty, it hadn't mattered in my life till then, it wasn't relevant in my conversations. The India I was seeing for the first time now was one of a sapping poverty that forced women to sell themselves for fifty rupees, or even just the cost of a meal, or some milk for their infant; a poverty of means but also of human contact, it was an emptiness. I had never encountered real poverty before, nothing beyond the scratching of a beggar on my car window, baby at her breast, as I waited for the lights to change, the endless time when you can neither look away nor make eye contact. I was a person well off, dealing with the well-off, advising them on how to become even more well off, and I had begun to feel uneasy about it. I was experiencing a quiet creeping sadness deep within me.

It was dawning on me that my training with McKinsey, my inherent attitude that I was a great problem solver, would not get me very far. If that was all I came equipped with, it was inadequate. I had a glimmer of insight, not yet formed into a plan, that we could move forward only by asking the way and working with the people who lived with the problem every day.

I had started seeing in these communities a resilience, strength, humour, heroism, and much else in the face of cruel circumstances, and it gave me inspiration and a feeling of hope and optimism. It put my problems in perspective, and they seemed very small. I was starting to feel a flame flickering inside me. Something had fanned the embers. Holding the hand of a wretchedly poor sex worker was to exchange existences ever so briefly with her. I saw young men with their lives falling apart and sometimes felt a stab, realizing that they were the same age as my sons. Ultimately it was the feelings of fellowship and kindness that enabled me to cope, and keep on moving.

We continued to move forward, learning furiously, by continuously engaging with field realities. And there is nothing more obviously real than a brothel, so vital to HIV prevention.

4

The Importance of Brothels

The brothel building we were entering in Kamathipura, in the heart of Mumbai, looked like it might collapse any minute, and I was not reassured as we climbed up three flights of creaking steps, in almost complete darkness. It was the time of early evening when the sex workers performed puja before their chosen gods, before the night's work began. The recital of arati, the tinkling of hand bells, and the sweet-pungent smell of agarbatti filled the air. At one landing a youngster, perhaps sixteen, was in seasoned negotiation with a woman just a few years his senior. The woman held a Pomeranian dog that had been dipped in henna and was a commanding red-orange. The dog growled menacingly at the teenager. As we entered the set of three rooms owned by the madam, a client stepped out, glaring at us as he pulled on his shirt. He seemed to insinuate – what's a brothel coming to these days if a paying customer is pushed out because some sahib types are visiting?

Priyabai was resplendent in a purple silk sari with heavy gold zari work. Faux gold bangles and chains flashed as she shifted her ample frame around in the small sofa. 'I came to Kamathipura from Sangli [four hundred kilometres to the south] when I was only a child. I had to work for six years without pay so that my malkin could earn back what she had paid for me. I couldn't even go to the bathroom without an older girl accompanying me, and I hardly ever saw the light of day. Then for the next six years I was in a fifty–fifty arrangement with the malkin, where I got to keep half my earnings. After that I worked my way up, till I became a malkin myself.' She narrates her story with complete ease, as though all this was a simple rite of passage.

'I don't keep women prisoners, like my malkin did with me,' Priyabai continued. 'My girls are like my daughters and are free to go any time.' I was not really convinced. Priyabai may have been an exception, but scores of women were being trafficked into Mumbai's brothels every day. The infamous cages in which women were once displayed in Kamathipura had largely disappeared, but the system of bonded labour in the first phase of a sex worker's career was still in place when we worked with the women there.

'Kamathipura is dying,' rued Priyabai. 'Real estate is booming, and brothel owners are selling out. Kamathipura has also been stigmatized by the HIV scare, and customers are nervous about coming here. Come back in ten years and there will be no Kamathipura, only fine offices here.' She was lamenting what would be the end of what she perceived was a great institution.

Priyabai need not have despaired. Kamathipura is just a stone's throw from Mumbai's elegant Marine Drive, and in the 1980s is said to have housed over a hundred thousand workers.[1] When we worked in Kamathipura there were fewer than ten thousand. It may be on a decline, but you wouldn't know that if you happened to stroll along Grant Road which is in the heart of Kamathipura, close to Mumbai Central railway station.

Brothels are indeed an endangered species in India. They tend to be in prime real estate locations, and the option to sell is attractive. Then there is the pressure from those who believe a brothel is a sinful abomination, and that such establishments should be summarily shut down. The most notorious manifestation of that attitude was the razing of the thriving brothel on Baina beach in Goa without much warning by government-ordered bulldozers in 2004. If sex workers are dispersed it is difficult to get HIV prevention services to them. Large, well-regulated, legal brothels are a boon for HIV prevention.

In India the extent of commercial sex practised in brothels was only about 7 per cent, with the bulk of it practised off the street and from homes.[2] But because women in brothels saw many more clients it was an important variant of commercial sex work that needed to be addressed.

~

The most celebrated global example of legalized, closely monitored brothels to prevent the spread of HIV is Thailand in the 1990s. By 1994, 1.6 per cent of adults in Thailand were HIV positive and the primary mode of transmission was unprotected commercial sex. HIV prevalence in sex workers was about 18 per cent.[3] Dance bars and massage parlours, thin covers for commercial sex work, proliferated in Bangkok and other major cities. Most of the sex work happened in these facilities. In those days visiting a sex worker was an accepted social norm among Thai men.

The Thai government decided that the spread of the virus had to be stopped at any cost, and appointed a senior cabinet minister, Senator Viravaidya Mechai, to lead the campaign. The Thai programme had two reinforcing elements – creating condom awareness and enforcing a 100 per cent condom usage policy (CUP) in facilities. Government inspectors would literally count used condoms every day, and match these against transactions recorded in the brothel's books. A third infraction meant the facility would be immediately shut down. Women working in these facilities were required to have a mandatory STI check-up every month.[4] A woman doctor who worked extensively in Thailand jokingly described it to me as an assembly line of women with legs spread, so quickly and efficiently were the check-ups done.

By the turn of the millennium, condom usage among sex workers had reached 95 per cent in Thailand. HIV prevalence in sex workers had been brought down to 2 per cent. Prevalence in the general population had come down to less than 1 per cent. Mechai's programme demonstrated that vulnerability to HIV could be tackled when sex work was amassed in a few identifiable places, where the programme could work with the owners. It also helped that in Thailand tough measures to enforce condom use, which would have been challenged by civil society groups in many countries, were acceptable.

In early 2003, my colleague Alkesh and I went to Bangkok to study the Thai programme. We were fortunate to get an appointment with Senator Mechai and as we were leaving I asked him the question uppermost in my mind: 'Senator, in India commercial sex work is hardly practised in brothels. The sex worker is invisible – dispersed on the streets and in homes. On the streets they do not solicit openly and are not readily identifiable. How should we contain the epidemic in such a setting?'

Mechai thought for a moment. Then, reaching forward, extending his hand, smiling wryly, he said, 'Good luck.' Our interview was over.

~

In India, large brothels in identifiable red-light areas are rare. The prominent ones are Kamathipura in Mumbai, Budhwar Peth in Pune, Sonagachi in Kolkata, and GB (Garstin Bastion) Road in Delhi. Many towns in India have brothels on a smaller scale. In other regions of India the brothel is a home, often in respectable residential areas, housing three to five women, where sex work is practised. The permanent fixture in these mini-brothels is the owner, who is always a woman. The madam will take in women to practise sex work from her home daily, or she may house them for months. She takes a cut from each transaction.

In Ballapuram in West Godavari district of coastal Andhra Pradesh, we visited a home-based brothel of a special kind. The house had three tiny rooms, a kitchen, and a small courtyard. Four generations of one family lived together there. They were a grandmother, simply known to everyone as Amma, her daughter Kanta in her mid-thirties, Kanta's daughter Shobha, about eighteen, and Shobha's child, a one-year old boy. Kanta ran the home-based business. She was beautiful, with fine features, light brown eyes, and olive complexion.

We were sitting with the whole family in the common area of the house, doors shut so that we would not be disturbed. Commercial sex was a way of life for Kanta, the only dependable, steady source of income to keep her household going. Kanta ran the family business with tight efficiency. She also took in a few women residents, on a short-term basis, but generally avoided quick in–out daily transactions by street-based sex workers. She explained how her cash flow worked, her pricing system, and how she managed the local constabulary and goons.

While we were talking, there was a knock on the door. Kanta shouted out that they were not open for business, but the frustrated client would not go away. The knocking became louder and more insistent, as though he was in a state of desperate emergency. Sighing, and at a signal from her mother, Shobha got up to handle the client. After a loud discussion, during which Shobha berated a now-contrite client, they disappeared into an inner room, and she emerged in less than five minutes, with an apologetic smile. Our conversation picked up, without losing a beat, from where it had been interrupted.

'All of us are in sex work,' Kanta said, as her mother and daughter nodded eagerly. 'In fact, if a man comes here, he has a choice all in one family, the old and the new. Where can you get that?' she laughed. Life was not as easy as Kanta's joking manner valiantly tried to suggest. When I met her four years later she had aged prematurely and looked haggard almost beyond recognition.

~

In Sonagachi in central Kolkata, we learnt a lot from Dr Smarajit Jana's renowned HIV prevention programme. Where Thailand's was essentially a top-down model, Sonagachi used a grassroots community-based approach.

Sonagachi in 2004 was a series of streets and narrow alleys, where more than ten thousand women from all over India practised commercial sex. The large brothel area had separate sections for women from different states. Here, there would be a little Andhra Pradesh and there, Punjabi, Uttar Pradesh, and Nepali sections. Sweets, savouries, and even glossy magazines from those regions were on sale in many of these sections. Hot poha could be had in the Maharashtrian area and steaming momos in the Nepali section. These regional units were maintained so that the women could feel at home and to make it easy for clients who have preferences for women from certain communities. Not all women stayed fixed in one area – there were free floaters as well, who chose to move around. Each section was a series of houses, from single-room cubicles barely bigger than a bed to units with a couple of bedrooms and a living room, sofas, and large-screen TVs. Typically, the houses were owned by madams, who rented the rooms out by the hour to street-based sex workers, or took a cut from the earnings of women who stayed for a longer term.

We arrived at Sonagachi in the late evening of a hot summer day in 2003, and it was as if we had stepped into a carnival. The lanes were crowded with customers who defied categorization. There was the government babu stopping by for a quick one before he went home to his loving wife and children. Small-time businessmen from out of town, seeking to unwind after a hard day's work. Dhoti-clad lovers of art, come to enjoy an evening of ghazal and mujra. Men of affluence who stepped gingerly out of chauffeured cars. And even a few foreign tourists, keen to discover all that India had to offer.

Like actors in a great stage show, the sex workers of Sonagachi were displayed in every possible style, matching the diversity of their clients. They were a riot of colour. A woman with plump thighs in a red micro-skirt had her arm linked with her friend in a gaudy sari. A gaggle of hijras, with exaggeratedly painted lips and impossibly narrow waists, stood with casually flung pallus magically sliding down their bosoms. Small groups of male sex workers offered cigarettes, some broad-chested and macho, others delicately feminine.

Meanwhile, the brokers for the women in residence up the flights of stairs sidled up. 'The real action isn't here, babu – you look like a bhadralok – come with me, I'll take you to the real action, just upstairs.' Street vendors purveying hot pakoras, NGO kiosks offering free condoms, and a group of performing acrobats completed the scene of unrestrained and macabre celebration.

Our assigned guide that day was Debu, thirty, the son of a sex worker who had practised at Sonagachi and passed away, an early victim of HIV. He was watching us closely to gauge our reaction and asked with some pride, 'What do you think of our Sonagachi, Ashokji? There is nothing like this anywhere in India.' I nodded, smiling in assent. Indeed, as we were to find out that day, Sonagachi was in many ways a wonderland for sex workers.

~

Our host Dr Jana was the tiny bespectacled architect of Sonagachi's community-based HIV intervention programme, clearly its father figure and authority from behind the scenes. In 1995 NACO had asked Jana to create a model HIV prevention programme at Sonagachi. He was convinced that the Thailand model of 'targeted intervention' was flawed. He believed a better way was to mobilize the sex worker community and turn over the ownership of the programme to the sex workers themselves. Ten years later, Sonagachi had become a globally celebrated success. The sex workers' collective that Jana created at Sonagachi is called Durbar Mahila Samanwaya Cooperative – DMSC or Durbar (meaning unstoppable in Bengali) for short. Durbar has three parts: service provision (outreach services, clinics), a cooperative bank, and a cultural wing.

The next morning, we visited one of Durbar's clinics. It was a clean facility, its record-keeping diligent. A doctor attended to a handful of sex workers who were awaiting their turn calmly. The nurse in attendance and the record-keepers – in fact, all the meagre staff apart from the doctor – were also practising sex workers. They bustled about, getting first-time patients to fill out their forms, with no proof of identity required.

In the afternoon we met with the twelve-member governing council of Durbar's cooperative bank. The council members were all sex workers. Shipra Das, the eloquent chairperson, explained how it worked. 'Nearly every woman in DMSC has an account at the cooperative bank. We ask each woman to deposit ten rupees every day in her account. The money is picked up by a boy that the bank sends around, because it is difficult for the women to come to the bank every day. It's the regularity of deposit that is important, so that saving becomes a habit. Sex workers have a way otherwise of spending all their daily earnings, leaving nothing for an emergency.' Additionally, the bank was the fulcrum for Sonagachi's activities, ensuring that sex workers stayed.

Turning to a young sex worker at the back of the room – not part of the council – I asked, 'Can you explain how this bank keeps you safe from HIV?' She replied confidently, 'When my child was sick, and I needed a hundred rupees for medicine I took it out of the five hundred rupees I had saved. Otherwise I would have had to have sex without a condom with a customer, to make the extra money that day. I was always living hand to mouth before the bank was made.'

Meeting over, we were entertained by Rasika, DMSC's dance troupe. It had a dozen performers, both women and transgenders, all sex workers. They were dressed in matching costumes of red and black, the women wearing saris and the transgenders in kurta-pyjama. We watched a dance-and-music sequence called *Oi Mahila Ke* ('Who Is That Woman?') that depicted the eternal aspects of woman – wife, mother, and sex worker. I was captivated by the performance, which was sensitively portrayed and exquisitely choreographed in classical Bharatanatyam. I learnt that Rasika had performed to acclaim in major cities in India and abroad. I was told, amid laughter, that on one such trip to Geneva, they had a crisis when their star performer, a transgender, found a client and could not be traced for a couple of days.

~

Admirably, the Sonagachi programme prevented minors from appearing in the trade. Any girl suspected of being a minor was reported by the community to one of the several NGOs working in the brothel. Incidentally, a minor had been found just that day, and before I knew it, I was led into a closed room.

A child who looked no more than twelve was sitting on a bed, closely hugging an NGO worker. When she saw me she cringed, hiding her face in the worker's sari. It was obvious she was frightened to death by the sight of a man. I quickly turned and rushed out of the room. It appeared there was no place to send her, because the parents who had sold her into the trade would not want her back. It was the same problem with children – what to do after you save them – though in a different context from what I had seen in Imphal, with Danny.

I learnt that there was both altruism and a dose of savvy business thinking in the saving of children at Sonagachi. With a certain type of man, a youngster, especially a virgin, would command a much higher price than would the regulars. Keeping children out also reduced competition.

~

Sonagachi taught us much about what to do and what to avoid doing. Sonagachi had kept HIV infection levels among its sex workers at single-digit levels, a remarkable achievement in a brothel setting. Kamathipura and other large brothel areas had not managed to do that. Sonagachi was proof of how powerful community involvement is in HIV prevention. We saw how communities of sex workers – traditionally treated as helpless victims by many prevention programmes – can be empowered to be the prime agents of change.

In the process, they can organize themselves to deliver services safely, address the root causes of their vulnerability, and develop an essential self-esteem. The importance of community was the single biggest learning for us from Sonagachi.

The criticism of the Sonagachi model is that it has never been replicated anywhere else, even in brothel settings. One reason then was that the programme was not well documented. There was very little by way of standard operating procedures that NGOs and governments could use elsewhere. The other was that it was excessively personality-dependent – Jana's. It seemed that behind the scenes he had a hand in every decision, big or small, and his word was final. I learnt that charismatic leaders need to make themselves obsolete, and not behave like benevolent dictators, if communities are to sustain on their own.

The most crucial difference was that Sonagachi, like Patpong in Bangkok, was largely a long-established brothel area. Aggregation of dispersed street sex workers, which is the main challenge facing HIV programmes all over India, was much less of an issue in Sonagachi.

~

Brothelized sex was only a small part of sex work. In most places across the country it was practised mainly on the street and to a lesser extent in homes. In many cases the sex worker was moving from place to place. The key question was how to bring these women to a single point that was *not* a brothel, a challenge we will come back to later in this narrative.

We were discovering that the main challenge in HIV prevention in India was the fact that sex workers were effectively invisible.

5

The Invisible Consumer

Every business strives to understand its customers – who the buyers are, where they can be found, what makes them buy the product. This kind of thinking is at the heart of any business, whether soap or steel, ice cream or iPhone.

In Avahan we too were dealing with a consumer product – HIV prevention services. We were entering a huge market, setting up our programme offices in eighty-three districts in six states, covering over 650 towns. In each town we first had to estimate the number of consumers – primarily the sex workers. We then needed to understand how many practised their trade on the street, in homes, or in brothels. We needed to know, for each of these categories, how many sex transactions they had every week. We had to know how often they used or did not use condoms. It was essential to know how many already had HIV or other STIs. Without this micro-level data, we would be shooting in the dark. We had to understand the transaction between sex worker and client in intimate detail.

There is a simple fact we had to keep in mind: all sex workers are not the same. A few, who are the ones most vulnerable, account for a disproportionate share of HIV infections. If there was data that allowed us to focus much more on those sex workers, delivery would be far more efficient, and impact would be much greater.

That is why we were travelling across hundreds of our locations, talking to sex workers, trying to understand the contexts in which they lived and worked, and what drove their risky behaviour. Our initial focus was on female sex workers, because they constituted the largest number of highly at-risk people. At first, our travels were only surface deep, across states and towns, but we increasingly did deeper dives, staying longer in different places.

The diversity of female sex work we discovered was staggering. In most parts of India, sex work was being practised mainly from the street, or in homes, and there was a lot of migration. The women were dispersed, moving, and typically did not present themselves as sex workers in an obvious way. In effect they were invisible, blending perfectly into the general population.

~

Time and again, we met the sex worker who seemed a typical middle-class housewife but took on a few clients a month at her house. This could be without her husband knowing, sometimes with his pretending he didn't know, and sometimes with his active collusion.

Chennai is India's fourth largest city with a population of eleven million. We were headed for CHES, an NGO funded by USAID's AIDS Prevention and Control Project (APAC), which worked with female sex workers in Chennai. Like many NGOs working in HIV prevention, they used the services of practising sex workers – known as peer workers, or simply peers – to reach other sex workers. The peers would convey messages about safe sex, provide condoms, and encourage the women to seek treatment for ulcerative STIs such as syphilis which fuelled the transfer of HIV.

The peer workers showed us their mapping of sex work in a certain well-known upper-middle-class residential area of Chennai, home to several foreign embassies and trendy restaurants. The mapping covered most of the neighbourhood, divided into five zones, house by house. There was a map on chart paper for each zone, hand-drawn with a marker by the peer responsible for that area. Sex work spots were marked by red dots, while condom drop-off points were in blue.

This conservative section of central Chennai was a rash of red dots! 'This house is used for sex work . . . this bus stop normally has two sex workers in the rush hour . . . this car, usually parked outside this temple, picks up clients and follows these routes . . . these lodges take in sex workers . . .' The peer continued for about half an hour, describing how sex workers, brokers, police, pimps, and clients all connected in an ecosystem of mutual dependence.

There was clearly a lot of sex work going on, and it could be pinpointed by someone who was in the business – and yet it was all invisible. In most parts of India, we were discovering that sex work is practised mainly on the street, in street-linked lodges, or in homes.

As I looked at the maps, it occurred to me that this level of understanding of where each type of sex worker was located, and at which times, would have been a gold standard in many a retail business wanting to know its customers.

~

In the bustling temple town of Madurai in Tamil Nadu I met thirty-year-old Kasturi, a 'secret sex worker', one of the thousands of women in India who covertly practise commercial sex to keep their families going. Her story is typical:

'My father abandoned our family when I was eight. I had two younger sisters and my mother worked very hard. She was a vegetable vendor. I studied up to third standard, and when I was eighteen I was married to my maternal uncle.[1] I had three children in the first five years. From the beginning, my husband liked to drink, and he didn't like to work. He was a contract labourer, in a factory making plastic vessels. He made 3000–4000 rupees a month and spent most of it on country liquor. The children and I were always hungry. I didn't have money to even provide them with milk regularly. Once our youngest daughter had a high fever, and I could not afford to take her to a doctor. I asked my husband for money and got a hard kick that knocked me across the room. Desperately, I turned to a friend to borrow the money. She shared a secret with me – that she was a part-time sex worker, and that changed my life.'

Kasturi's eyes were shining with tears and she was agitated as she relived the experience.

'"Why do you make it so hard on yourself?" my friend asked. She offered to introduce me to a nice man, Anand, later that day at her place. I went there that evening, terrified and ashamed. When the man came in I shrank into a corner. "Why are you crying?" Anand asked after we had sex. "You are only doing this because you need the money." He gave me four hundred rupees, much more than the usual price, of which I gave 150 to my friend. After that I started standing quietly for clients on the streets in that area and had an arrangement with a nearby lodge to bring in clients for thirty minutes each.

'I always meet Anand in my friend's house. He is married and devoted to his wife and two children, and often talks to me about them. It has been five years now since he became a regular customer. He sometimes gives me small gifts, like this pair of earrings. He always treats me with respect, and I love him. Besides him, I see three other men on a regular basis, sometimes at the lodge or at my friend's place. I see each man twice a month and the money I earn keeps my children healthy. Now I don't have to stand on the street any more and pick up men I don't know. These men will never tell, and no one suspects that I am a secret sex worker. My husband thinks I do social work with an NGO. I worry that one day he will find out, and that would be terrible – after all, the children need a father. Only my mother knows. She accepts that it's the only way I can manage my household.'

~

Dr Tachi Yamada was the urbane, soft-spoken president of Global
Health at the Gates Foundation, and my boss from 2006 onward. On
his first visit to Avahan we took him to meet sex workers in Guntur, a
town of about 750,000 inhabitants in coastal Andhra Pradesh. Such
meetings are typically held sitting cross-legged on the ground in the
office of the NGO, and Tachi struggled a bit, as had I in my initial days
with Avahan. The sex workers trusted the NGO staff, and twenty-six
of them had readily agreed to come and meet with us. Many of them
were in flashy bright saris and wore showy bangles and necklaces, all
dressed up for the meeting with an important foreigner.

'But these aren't poor women, they seem more like middle-class
people!' Tachi said at the end of the lively meeting. He was both
right and wrong. Many women starting out in sex work are destitute.
Thrown out of her home by her abusive husband, small baby at her
breast, living on the pavement, is a frequently encountered profile. To
survive, the women turn to sex work.

How quickly they rose in the profession depended on how young,
pretty, fair-skinned, and street-smart they were. If they got four or
five clients, they could be earning as much as 500–800 rupees a day. It
may take a woman a couple of years to get to that level of earning, or
she may never get there, in which case she would stay destitute. That
daily wage was about three times what a labourer working the whole
day under the hot sun could then earn. It would indeed put her by
financial classification into the low end of India's middle class.[2] They
could well afford to buy a couple of glitzy saris for the special occasion.

They were not equivalent to middle-class women, though, in other
respects. If a woman was known to be a sex worker most landlords
would be unwilling to take her in as a tenant – or they might, if free
sex on demand was thrown in. Kindergarten schools would not admit
her children. She may not get a ration card, because she could not
produce a proper proof of address. She would face regular harassment
and even violence from local goons and the police. She would always
be living on the edge.

If Tachi had looked closely, he would have seen that the fancier women typically sat in front. Towards the back were the more ragged, unkempt women, often staring into space, unwilling to speak. Mainly, these women were new entrants into the trade, utterly poor, living on the streets. So a room full of sex workers would have a mix of very poor to middle-class women. Most of these women had 'husbands' or boyfriends, and often these were symbiotic relationships. Having her own man had its distinct benefits for a sex worker – for example, he would negotiate with landlords. In return, the man got a steady income from the sex worker, at least enough to keep him in drink. Having a 'husband' helped her get her child into school. Sex workers are often caring mothers and will not hesitate to spend on their child's school fees and books.

So the money the sex workers earned disappeared quickly, and they ended up living day to day, with a high level of financial and emotional insecurity.

~

In December 2002, after that first field visit to Vizag, we flew west to Hyderabad, then the capital of Andhra Pradesh, 650 kilometres away. At the time we worked there, Andhra Pradesh was one of India's major states, with a population of over 75 million. Andhra Pradesh then had an adult HIV prevalence that was the highest among Indian states at 2.2 per cent.

Hyderabad sits in the centre of the Deccan Plateau, and had a population of 4.2 million people. The city lies along the banks of the Musi River and is defined by its rocky hills with their arresting stone formations. North and South India meet in Hyderabad, as do a variety of Indian cultures, and Islamic and Hindu traditions. The architecture of Hyderabad combines Mughal, colonial, and Indo-Saracenic styles, with contrasting yet complementary structures often standing right next to each other.

In Hyderabad we visited an NGO that intervenes with sex workers in the city centre. Two peer workers and two male outreach workers led us through the crowded area around the railway station. Regular clients of sex workers will generally recognize a sex worker, even when she is off duty, and I could see that the peer workers we were with were receiving the whispered proposition every so often as they made their way through the crowd. It was a problem finding a place where we could talk to sex workers on the street without drawing unwanted attention to them, so the NGO had arranged for us to meet them upstairs in a middle-class cafeteria. The place had only a handful of customers when we went in, mainly men from the locality, taking a break for a hot chai before getting back to work.

Ten minutes after we sat down six women came up the stairs. To all appearances they were conservative, modestly dressed middle-class housewives. My young teammate leaned forward and asked the outreach workers, 'Are these your family . . .?' Like me, he too was puzzled why they should want to make this a family occasion.

We were in for a surprise – these middle-class housewives were really sex workers. By this time, more were arriving, in groups of two or three. A half-dozen settled at our table, while the others ordered tea at adjoining tables and talked with my two colleagues. It looked like a kitty-party. One of the women at my table, Sarla, had an oversized bindi, large plastic glasses, her hair in a severe bun, and pallu draped modestly around her shoulders. She could have passed for a schoolteacher. Her friend Bina was demure, young, and pretty, and wore a pink chiffon sari. I found it awkward to ask these housewives – though they were sex workers – the kind of questions we had to ask. That was only day two of my first field trip, and I had not got used to the open and direct conversation that sex workers were comfortable with.

'I do this work off and on,' said Bina. 'My husband believes I work in a long-distance phone booth collecting fees.' Sarla told us that she did sex work because her daughter was studying for a master's in chemistry and the fees were high and her son in the eighth grade needed a computer. I couldn't get my mind around the fact that these women sold their bodies to keep their lower-middle-class households going, and to take care of their children's higher education. The situation was closer to home than I had ever thought possible.

At other tables there were women who needed the money just to get by. One of them told my colleagues that her husband knew she was seeing clients and they had worked out a code to spare them any embarrassment. It was understood that the client would leave his slippers outside the house. If the husband came home early and saw the slippers, he would go somewhere else.

Meanwhile, I was getting concerned because by now about twenty poor and middle-class housewife–sex workers had filled the tiny cafeteria – and more were coming in. The NGO clearly had a lot of influence and was intent on demonstrating that! But the waiters had begun to whisper, and the regular customers were staring. I called the interviews to an abrupt halt and thanked the ladies for spending time with us. I looked over the balcony and saw Sarla and Bina walking down the steps. Two demure, middle-class housewives faded into the crowd.

The episode had a sad postscript. Minutes after we left, the police, tipped off by a waiter, raided the cafeteria. The women there were hauled off to the police station and treated roughly. The NGO had the influence to get them released in a few hours, but I resolved to never again meet with sex workers in a public location.

~

In India, sex work is not a criminal offence, but open solicitation is. So it is rare to find 'painted women' on the streets, except outside major brothels. There is a system of signalling that sex workers and the men who look for sex workers understand. For instance, the signal could be the colour of flowers she wears in her hair or the way she holds her handbag across her shoulder. The simplest method is eye contact. An Indian woman will not hold eye contact with a stranger – if there is eye contact by chance, she will quickly look away. A woman standing on the street who consistently holds eye contact for a few seconds, more than once, could well be a sex worker. The street sex worker will also give her mobile phone number to a few of her regular clients.

Having established the connection, and completed a hurried negotiation, the sex worker and her client might use an abandoned building or even go behind some bushes. Otherwise they will go to a nearby lodge, the customer following some ten feet behind the sex worker. She will have an arrangement with the lodge owner, who will receive a cut and be willing to rent out a room on an hourly basis.

~

Kolhapur is a busy commercial city in southern Maharashtra, with a population of about 550,000. Sex work flourishes here, especially in the area around the large interstate bus depot. The peer worker from the local NGO that Avahan was funding introduced us to Swati, a secret street sex worker. She in turn led us to Tarun Lodge, where we met the owner himself. Mr Tarun was in his mid-forties, dapper, wearing a checked shirt and nicely creased jeans. He had sparkling white teeth and exuded an unbearably sweet perfume and had a way of clasping your hand and moving up close, speaking in a low voice, occasionally glancing over his shoulder nervously. His perfume was making me giddy, and I made vain attempts to free myself from his firm grasp and take a few steps back, but without giving offence.

Mr Tarun was proud of his establishment. He made it sound as if he was engaged in some form of social service. He led us up a flight of stairs and showed us one of the rooms. It was small and clean, dimly lit by a single overhead bulb, and with just about space for a bed and a small side desk. There was a tiny attached toilet. 'We change the sheets after every customer,' he said earnestly. Clearly, this was the marker of a classy sex-lodge. 'There is a room boy always on call who can make available drinks, peanuts, anything else.' He gestured towards a lad of about fourteen who had been trailing us. 'We are always fully occupied, almost twenty-four hours. We have customers from all over India because of the bus stand. Even a few foreigners.' At this he leered, rubbing his thumb and two adjacent fingers together, the universal gesture meaning 'they have money'.

~

From Delhi it takes twenty hours to get to Kakhandi, a village with a population of about 1200, in Bijapur district in northern Karnataka. I was travelling with Bill Gates Senior and his wife Mimi, who were visiting India to understand the Avahan programme, in 2004. Bill Senior was then in his late seventies and cut an imposing figure, six feet six inches tall. Apart from the difference in height, father and son looked almost exactly alike.

We left Delhi by the evening flight to Bangalore, 2200 kilometres south. The next morning, we took the Deccan Airways flight to Belgaum, covering the distance of 520 kilometres in ninety minutes, in a DC-10 turboprop. At Belgaum, our rugged Toyota Qualis was waiting, and we set off on a road full of potholes, to the town of Bijapur, 210 kilometres east of Belgaum. As we drove west to east, the landscape changed from lush green fields and rich black earth to the parched red soil of Bijapur. There we met up with the local NGO workers and set out for the small village of Kakhandi, deep in Bijapur district, on the southern border of Maharashtra, arriving two hours later.

Kakhandi had about 250 houses. It was a mazelike criss-cross of alleys. A large peepul tree encircled by a cement platform stood next to the panchayat centre. That the villagers treated the tree as sacred was evident from the strings of thick saffron and red threads tied around the trunk and hanging from low branches. Village elders sat idly on the cement platform in the shade of the tree, fanning themselves in the scorching heat by twirling a piece of cloth, slowly consuming their midday meal of spicy flat-beans, chutney podi, and jawar roti, staple foods of North Karnataka. It was the monsoon season but there was not even a hint of rain clouds in the white-blue sky. We passed the anganwadi centre where preschool kids were squatting on the floor. A tyke sat in one corner crying, refusing to eat, despite the cajoling of the anganwadi worker. It is a scene that plays out across the world – first day in school.

Walking past tiny dwellings and kirana stores, we reached the outskirts of the village and walked some thirty metres to the much smaller Dalit section, demarcated by a line made with white lime powder. It forcefully brought home to us that even today the caste system is strongly prevalent in India's villages and the lowest castes are restricted to their own section, with their own well.

We had travelled this far to meet with members of the traditional Devadasi sex worker community, but we found that most of the sex workers were out of town. We met with six Devadasi women sitting on the floor of the hut of Janakiamma, their leader. 'There are about a hundred Devadasi women in this village,' said Janakiamma. 'Of these, ninety practise sex work, and currently seventy are away in different parts of Maharashtra – Miraj, Sangli, Satara, Solapur, Pune, Mumbai.'

One of the women, Koila, spoke up. She looked about fifty. 'Everyone goes to Maharashtra to make money, but I have decided not to any more. You can go there and make money and run the risk of dying [she was referring to HIV], or stay here, stay alive, and try to manage somehow.'

Stepping into her hut, we saw that it was furnished comfortably with cane furniture and a small TV set. On the wall there was a framed black-and-white picture of a policeman in uniform, with a garland of flowers around it. Puzzled, I asked who that was, and Koila explained that that was her husband. Seeing our surprise, she clarified, 'He is married, but also to me. He has taken care of me for twenty years now.'

Corridor of HIV transmission from North Karnataka into Maharashtra

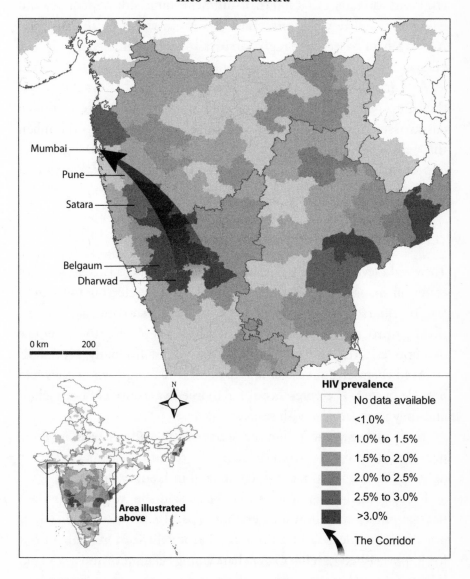

Mumbai

Pune

Satara

Belgaum

Dharwad

0 km   200

N

Area illustrated above

HIV prevalence

No data available

<1.0%

1.0% to 1.5%

1.5% to 2.0%

2.0% to 2.5%

2.5% to 3.0%

>3.0%

The Corridor

Koila was obviously in a minority, having the security of a devoted, long-term 'husband'. Districts like Bijapur are prone to drought and depend desperately on the monsoon rain for their meagre crops. If the monsoon fails – as it did that summer – hundreds of poor peasant women set out north to practise sex work in richer locales in south Maharashtra to earn enough to sustain their families back in the village.

As I moved around the other districts in North Karnataka, and then into Maharashtra, it felt as though there was a well-trodden passage, stretching all the way to the large cities of Pune and Mumbai, through which the sex workers moved up and down, chasing better opportunities. We started calling it the Corridor, and reckoned that it would be about five hundred kilometres long.

~

The word Devadasi roughly means 'handmaiden of God'. The Devadasi tradition spans several centuries – an inscription referring to them in the Yogimara Caves of modern Madhya Pradesh dates back to the third century BC. Devadasi girls are dedicated at puberty to the service of a goddess, Yellamma, and do not marry. Traditionally, Devadasis engaged themselves in music and dance in the temple where they had been dedicated. Their presence at ceremonies was considered auspicious and they were treated with respect.

There is a temple to Yellamma in Saundatti, a village of about 8500 people, ninety minutes from Belgaum. Here, girls are dedicated to the deity at the Saundatti festival, conducted in January each year.

Every Devadasi sex worker I spoke to said she would never want her daughters to follow in her footsteps. To the extent that it is practised, the Devadasi tradition has become little more than a front for impoverished parents to get their young daughters into sex work. When the girls reach puberty, their virginity is sold to the highest bidder and this launches them into a career in sex work. The price for an underage virgin, I was told, could run into hundreds of thousands of rupees. There are many men who consider that first sex highly auspicious and are willing to pay whatever it takes for the opportunity.

A few weeks later, wanting to better understand the Corridor, we drove 340 kilometres due north from Belgaum to Pune. It was monsoon time, heavy rains had swept across Maharashtra, and nature was at her verdant best. The hills of the Western Ghats had a dark velvet sheen, and the fields along the winding highway presented themselves in endless shades of green. A cool breeze blew, and we kept our windows down and breathed in the pure air that carried that special petrichor that comes with the Indian monsoon.

Shortly after we started, we stopped at a tiny impoverished hamlet of about twenty thatched houses, occupied only by Devadasi women. The rains had damaged many of the huts, and we trudged our way through soft mud. We entered a hut that had been partly destroyed. Blue tarpaulin and gunny bag covers were spread over missing sections of the roof, held down by the weight of a few bricks and stones.

It was small, about ten feet by twenty feet. There was a chulha on the mud floor in one corner, with a few pans and other utensils and a tiny kerosene stove around it. A few mats were rolled up and leaning against the wall. Two light bulbs hung from the mud roof.

Fifteen Devadasi women had gathered in the hut, and we squatted on the floor in the tiny space that was available. They were all older women, from their late forties up. It was apparent that the younger women had all left, travelling up the Corridor. The older women left behind made their living from begging, carrying the image of Yellamma and singing. They were a sombre lot, and there was almost no conversation.

Someone brought out two musical instruments of a kind I had never seen before. One was a type of ektara, sitar-like in shape, but much smaller. The other was more unusual – a small drum, open on top, with a single string inside running diagonally from the top lip of the drum to the opposite base. The drum was beaten on the side with a curved stick, while the string inside was plucked, a fascinating combination of a string and percussion instrument.

The women began to play the instruments as they sang to Yellamma, asking for her blessings. *'This life is an ocean, and you, the boat that can carry me.'*

~

Pune, with a population then of just over three million, is the ninth biggest city in India. I was almost at the end of the Corridor (the last stop would be two hundred kilometres further north – the brothels of Kamathipura in Mumbai). We sat on a durrie-covered floor on the third storey of a rickety building in Budhwar Peth, the brothel area of Pune, which housed more than six thousand women. Sitting in that airy room with a balcony, I was talking to eighteen women who worked in the area. 'How many of you are from Pune?' I asked. There was no show of hands. 'How many are from North Karnataka?' This time I counted fourteen raised hands, most of them Devadasis, wearing the black beaded necklace traditionally worn by women from their community. As I asked more questions, I learnt that they all came from the hundreds of small villages like Kakhandi in the North Karnataka districts that border southern Maharashtra. This also told us that sex workers rarely practise brothel-based sex in their home towns.

Most sex workers are migrants. The migration happens all the time, always from the poorer places to places with better business opportunity. It happens from villages to towns, and from towns to cities, all over India. Another such route we discovered is from western Andhra Pradesh to Guntur, an affluent town on the eastern coast. Sex workers from Guntur then find their way up to Delhi, to practise in the capital's GB Road brothels. There are many such corridors in India, but most HIV programmes thought only in terms of local areas and not of dynamic corridors of migration.

~

In the first year of Avahan I travelled extensively with my team, and we met almost every type of female sex worker. I met women who worked in brothels, off the streets, and from their homes. I encountered the starving and destitute, the middle-class and the more affluent sex workers. I met the bar girls of Mumbai, who are among the most exploited women in sex work. I met highway sex workers, who specialized in servicing truckers. I met the elegant women who kept the traditional courtesan system going in small parts of coastal Andhra Pradesh. Each group was a complex community and each had its intricate dynamics.

These communities were largely invisible. Many were highly mobile. Many of them were not interested in HIV prevention services, since they had more pressing concerns to deal with. Bringing HIV prevention services to massive numbers of people who were effectively invisible and not interested seemed an impossible task.

Thailand and Sonagachi taught us how brothels could be effectively used in HIV prevention, because the women were to be found all in one place. But we were finding out that brothel-based sex work was only a small component. The crux of the problem therefore was how to bring these dispersed women together at a single location. Something there had to be so attractive that they would flock to it. As the data began coming in, and we learnt to ask the sex workers for the answers, we started seeing light.

6

Leadership Secrets of the
Commercial Sex Worker

Leaving McKinsey in late 2002 was a bittersweet experience. There was the excitement of the new adventure that lay ahead mixed with the pangs of leaving a place that felt like home after seventeen years. The best times I had at the Firm were when a small band of us moved to India in 1992, exhilarated at the prospect of building a new practice in an economy that was in the middle of turbulent transition. Looking back at that period, and at other transitions in my career, I can see now how the idea of leaping into the great unknown had always held some fascination for me.

At McKinsey I learnt a certain essential way of problem-solving that started with breaking a problem down into discrete pieces ('issues') using rigorous logic and some intuition. We would then gather and analyse data to get to the heart of the issues, and this enabled us to come up with insightful solutions. We believed that with this approach you could address knotty issues in almost any industry. Today's consultant is far more specialized, but the core of using logic to solve a problem would still be relevant.

After a few months in the field, however, it was apparent that this

78

approach would take us only so far. The problem we were facing was like nothing I'd encountered before. It was the challenge of delivering a product to a consumer who was invisible, always moving around, and who didn't have a felt need for it. It was dawning on me that it was not we who could provide a solution, it was the consumer herself, because she was the one who lived with the problem.

The answer lay in saying those words that never would have come to my lips earlier: *I don't know the answer to this. How should we go about it?* Saying this to a client when I was with the Firm would have been career-limiting, to put it mildly.

~

Over the years I got a few invitations from different McKinsey offices to be a speaker on Values Day. This was a tradition at that time, where every McKinsey office in the world closed for business and all professional staff, from director to analyst, came together to reflect upon, and reaffirm, the Firm's values. Quaint as this sounds, we spent an entire day on such things as 'Client First', 'Commitment', 'Respect', and – one I love in particular – the 'Obligation to Dissent'. These ideals mean a lot to me and so, in 2005, when Sunil Sanghvi, a director in the Chicago office, invited me to come and speak about values on their Values Day, I accepted readily.

A Values Day speaker is usually a director, past or current, and the wise one will ruminate about his career and shamelessly, though always with good taste, share a few stories about how he or she was confronted with tough choices and was guided by the values. I thought I'd try something different. I intended to speak about the values I was discovering among female sex workers across India and to say that I had never met anyone in corporate life who measured up to the leadership qualities I found in those unlikely communities. I called my talk 'Leadership Secrets of the Commercial Sex Worker' and sent an outline in advance.

I was greeted in Chicago by an associate partner, a senior manager who is something like an acolyte to the partnership, who was leading the Values Day organizing team. He was shuffling his feet, and I sensed a 'good-but' statement coming. He began: 'We're all looking forward to your talk, Ashok, and I really like the way you approach it, really novel. It's very inspiring and all, but . . .' He was clearly struggling with the obligation to dissent. 'Yes?' I said helpfully.

'But, you know, can you tone it down a little? It's a bit raw in parts, and after all this is a Midwestern audience. People are more conservative, and some of them may feel uncomfortable. I think it's slightly risky'.

'Which parts did you find raw?' I asked gently.

'Well, when you talk about things like anal sex, and the bit about KY Jelly . . .' he said, colouring and resuming the shuffle. I was briefly tempted to say that where there is anal sex there might well be KY Jelly. But I could not be flippant, because the associate partner was obviously in distress. Instead I said, 'I'm inclined to take the risk, but if you really want, we can ask Sunil for his opinion.'

Sunil laughed it off. He told me that talking about sex made many people who worked in formal settings uncomfortable, and I should say whatever I felt like saying. So I did.

~

I began my talk describing how my world had changed:

'I once worked with corporate leaders. I now work with commercial sex workers – male, female, and transgender – all over India. In the process, I have redefined my notions of leadership. I once worked from client offices and boardrooms. I now work in places where paid sex is the main item of business. My friends say that I could write an excellent guidebook to the great brothels of India after this job.

'Years back, when I was a manager, I accompanied a director who addressed the leadership team of one of the world's premier consumer products companies. I recall we talked about organization and innovation. Recently I spoke to the top management team of the same company when they were visiting India. This time I made an impassioned plea for a massive donation of their wonderful sexual lubricant which was in short supply. They seemed embarrassed by their own product.

'It's been a strange journey! It has led me to appreciate that there are many faces to leadership.

'At the Firm, I was a student of leadership. I have discovered since that if you take the classic attributes of leadership, they are to be found in some unlikely places – for example, among those who have survived the commercial sex trade. These women stand out for their capacity to judge character and negotiate well. They survive because of their personal courage, charisma, and sense of humour. They are selfless. They exercise leadership in the highest sense of the word, and with a combination of attributes I have rarely seen in business leaders. I am frequently struck, and always inspired, by the leadership of the commercial sex worker.'

I delivered my talk uncensored and was gratified to receive a standing ovation at the end. My friend the associate partner, in the first row, was beaming.

~

Every time I met and interacted with sex workers I would ponder over a fundamental question: Why did sex workers show so many more leadership attributes than a business leader? The answer is straightforward – out of necessity. A business leader has as many leadership attributes as he needs to have, and in his circumstances, very often, just one or two might suffice. He may be a great visionary, but a bad executor. He may inspire people through his sheer passion, but often behave like a jerk. He could be a great builder of coalitions, but not an ideas person. Rarely does he have to be an all-rounder in terms of leadership attributes because he has enough people to cover for him.

The female sex worker does not have this luxury. Her world is far more complex, much more challenging. She must deal with emotional, health, and financial crises all the time. There is the constant threat of violence, and her first mission is really to survive. She has no power, but still must stay in control. She has no support system, but she must cope. She simply cannot win with just one or two shots in her game; she needs a whole repertoire. It's not the kind of leadership that manifests itself in single dramatic incidents; it is leadership that is happening every day, all the time, part of her life.

I reflected on the many facets of leadership, and human qualities, that I had been discovering in female sex workers – judgement, courage, negotiating skills, humour, and selflessness.

Sex workers are great judges of character

In the beginning, I wasn't sure how I should talk with a sex worker. I needed to find out how many clients she typically saw every week, what types of sex she had with them, how often she used a condom, what she charged, where she went for treatment if she had an STI, whether she drank before sex, and more. These questions each had a purpose – they gave me valuable data to gauge the extent of her vulnerability to HIV, and thereby provided pointers to a solution. My dilemma was how to ask these extremely intimate questions without giving offence. I learnt very soon that the simplest way was to ask the question directly, and you would get an immediate direct answer – if the sex worker trusted you.

In Sonagachi one winter afternoon, Dr Smarajit Jana and I entered a cold, dark room to talk with Rakhi, a sex worker. She had been told by her gharwali, the madam who ran that section of the brothel, that someone from an NGO would be coming to meet her and ask a few questions. She didn't know that the unassuming-looking man before her was the person who had created the Sonagachi programme.

The busy time for a sex worker is generally from six in the evening onward. She may see the occasional client during the day, but for the most part of the afternoon she has free time to attend to personal matters. Rakhi was a migrant from Nepal, looked about twenty, and spoke adequate Bengali. Plump, fair-skinned – a premium feature for clients – with a doll-like face, she was painting her toenails a neon red with great concentration when we entered. Her long hair, still wet from a bath, was left open. An infant about three months old slept peacefully beside her.

The room wasn't large enough for anything but a bed, so we sat on the edge of her charpoy. We introduced ourselves, saying we had come to learn from her about her life in Sonagachi. Soon Jana embarked upon a series of extremely candid questions, all asked conversationally, and with respect. They spoke in Hindi for my benefit, since I don't know Bengali. I was struck by how direct the question–answer sequence was.

'How many customers do you see every day?' Rakhi put away her nail polish. 'Depends. Sometimes two, sometimes up to seven.'

'If you have ten encounters, in how many would the client use a condom?' Shushing her child who had begun to stir, Rakhi replied, 'Always do, with a customer, but not if it's my boyfriend.' In ten years with Avahan I rarely heard anything other than this 'I always do' answer.[1]

'Do you do anal sex?' Rakhi shook her head. 'I get asked sometimes, but I don't agree to that, even if he offers more money.'

'Do you have sex on all days of your period?' She was holding her baby to her chest, rocking him now. 'Except two days when the bleeding is very heavy,' she said. 'Do you use Long-Life [an imported red condom] to hide your period from the customer?' Rakhi looked up and smiled slowly, recognizing that this guy knew the trade. 'Sometimes, only they're expensive. But some clients actually like doing it during my monthly.' Rakhi had now put the baby to her breast, covering the infant with the pallu of her sari.

The conversation proceeded in this manner for about an hour. We were enjoying each other's company. There were occasional bawdy comments, with bursts of laughter. I was struck by how candid and direct Jana's questions were, and how readily Rakhi answered those questions. It was surprising how three perfect strangers could talk so intimately and in such a relaxed way.

Jana explained: 'Sex workers are tremendous judges of body language. They must develop that faculty to survive. They are, after all, a group of people who are exploited by almost everyone they meet – clients, pimps, madams, lovers. As a result, they don't trust anyone blindly. They must depend on their instincts about people, also because most are illiterate and can't rely on other faculties such as reading and acquired knowledge. So I find that they are amazing judges of people, especially of men. They can size you up in a moment, literally from twenty feet, and if they think you are a genuine person, and can trust you, they will be totally open with you. They speak without wasting time getting to the point, because time is also precious for them. Winning that trust is key if you want to work with these people.'

Rakhi didn't just trust Jana and me because her gharwali had introduced us. Instead, she had sized us up even as we introduced ourselves. There was no awkwardness in discussing the intimate details of sex, because sex was her trade and the most natural thing to discuss. Jana was showing respect for her profession by talking about its most intimate aspects in a way that conveyed that it was a choice she had had to make, it was perfectly acceptable – indeed it had to be respected.

Sex workers show great courage, even in dire circumstances

A woman in the sex trade will usually have a 'regular partner' – call him boyfriend, lover, or husband. The relationship is usually symbiotic. A husband enables the sex worker to find a landlord who will agree to rent a house. He provides her with some security from 'rowdies',[2] the stray men who randomly harass and molest sex workers. In return he often lives off the woman's earnings. He may have other regular sex partners. Sometimes, though, the relationship is one of genuine love. I came across several instances where a sex worker was tenderly cared for by a regular client, often an older, happily married man with kids of his own. These are complex relationships.

Love so often turns to hate, and this is where I have seen the courage, fortitude, survival instinct, and sheer heroism of sex workers. There is one story I will never forget. I was in Bangalore, at the sex worker community centre run by the NGO that implemented Avahan's programme in the heart of the lively city. The room had a dozen peer workers, and as usual we sat on the floor. I asked the sex workers when was the last time any of them had experienced an episode of violence, physical or emotional. The women told of their personal experiences of men who had cheated them, of police brutality, and of rejection by their families.

One woman had been quiet all along, listening intently, but not participating in the conversation. When asked if she would tell her story, she did so without hesitation, perhaps because no one had ever bothered to ask. I was shocked to see as she turned her head that her face was brutally scarred by acid. Her left eye had disappeared, and one side of her face was a ghastly mask, with deep serrations where the acid had done its work. Both her hands were damaged up to the elbows by the acid. The woman wore a threadbare thin cotton sari and looked about thirty. I had to force myself to look at her.

For the next several minutes, as she told her story, the woman wore the sweetest of smiles as she related her experience with violence. The smile never once left her face. 'My name is Parvati, and I don't do sex work any more. No man will approach me. I loved a man once, but our love turned to bitterness and hate. I suffered beatings every day, and when I finally left him he promised he would make me suffer.'

She paused to take a sip from a glass of water that a staff member offered. 'One day a gang of men descended on me and bundled me into an abandoned building, just off MG Road. They had been sent by my husband. They forced themselves on me, put horse's hair in my vagina, then chilli powder. Then they poured the acid on my face . . .'

As she spoke, still with a sweet smile on her face, a small tear came out of her good eye. I've seen many times that sex workers break down when they tell their stories, but more often they will have a smile fixed on their faces.

Parvati's strength in adversity was gut-wrenching. I flew back to Delhi that evening tired, very tired, still seeing that smile on the acid-scarred face.

Sex workers are good negotiators

It is not just business leaders who have to be adept at negotiating. A sex worker negotiates all the time with her clients for safe sex. She must be very good at it, because her life may literally depend on whether the man agrees to use protection.

At the height of the HIV epidemic why did men so often insist on unprotected sex? Often, the reason is that men are totally drunk when they go to a sex worker and throw all inhibition to the winds. Sex workers have stories of men who even allow the sex worker to put a condom on their penis, and then at the last minute pull it off and plunge right in.

I was in Chennai visiting the APAC HIV prevention programme, run by USAID. Dr R. Lakshmi bai, their charismatic, dynamic programmes and research manager, and I were talking with some of the APAC peer workers. Two of them were complete contrasts. One was plump and extroverted, and the other thin and shy. The plump one had us in splits as she play-acted the thin one's negotiation strategy. 'Oh no, sir, why would you want to have sex, why do you want to tire yourself out, when I can do something very special for you . . .?' All this, while the thin one, acting deeply embarrassed, tried to cover her face with her pallu.

'She's not all that shy as she's making out,' Lakshmi bai said. 'They all have advanced client negotiation skills. One trick they can depend on is oral sex rather than unprotected sex. Of course, they will still use a condom, preferably a flavoured one.' The sex worker negotiates the client down through a safer and safer sequence: sex with a condom, or oral sex, or a deluxe hand job. Success is if they can get the client to simply self-masturbate, and even better to get the man to fall asleep drunk when she gets paid for nothing, and he wakes up remembering nothing, but being assured that he performed like a tiger.

This condom negotiation is at the heart of HIV prevention. It is deadly serious, though with the client the sex worker will try to make it look like play. It could lead to violence and forced sex, especially if the sex worker had not sized up her client well or if she was not skilled in negotiation.

Sex workers have a sense of humour

Why is sense of humour a leadership quality? A sex worker's life is a tough one, and leaders adopt different ways to cope with adversity. Laughter is the sex worker's natural way of coping, an attitude that tells life that we refuse to be knocked down by you. They all seem to have a great sense of humour. They like to laugh, sing, dance, and drink with each other if someone in their group has had a windfall. So many of our meetings have dissolved when the group got bored, and someone just shouted out, 'Let's dance!' A drum would appear from nowhere, bawdy songs would be sung, and some would do a take-off on the latest dance moves of popular movie heroines.

Nishant Sharma, a young colleague in Avahan, was a good-looking chap, quiet and reserved. On a field trip in Andhra Pradesh we were sitting with a group of sex workers when one of them, Radha, spotted him and sized him up as someone she could easily tease and embarrass. Radha had flamboyant dark kajal in her eyes, and an exuberant bosom almost breaking the buttons of her blouse. She must have been about forty, more than fifteen years older than Nishant. As the discussion warmed up, some of us spotted her overtly fluttering her eyelashes and biting her lower lip as she stared directly at Nishant from across the room.

Nishant saw it too and was trying to keep his eyes down, turning redder by the minute. She whispered something to her friend, who came over to Nishant and stage-whispered loud enough for everyone to hear: 'Radha says she's wearing the female condom.' Nishant obviously didn't get the significance of this and said hoarsely that he didn't understand what that meant. A second message was conveyed from Radha: 'Radha says she wants to go inside with you.' By this time people had stopped talking to watch Nishant's discomfiture. As he shook his head from side to side, and kept his eyes on his feet, Radha sent a final message: 'Tell him I won't even charge anything, let's just be friends.' There were peals of laughter all around.

We have all borne the brunt of sex workers' jokes. I have more than once received marriage proposals, and mock ceremonies have been done on the spot ('we won't tell your wife!'). But I'll never forget the discomfiture of Dr James ('Jamie') Blanchard, a professor from the University of Manitoba, Canada, who were implementers of Avahan's work in Karnataka. He was then about forty, debonair, with a rosy complexion and wavy dark hair. A sex worker sidled up to him and got straight to the point. Someone translated – 'Smita says she wants to marry you.' Jamie turned beetroot red and stammered, 'Please tell her that I'm already m-married.' Pat came Smita's response: 'That's okay. Tell him I'm married too.'

Sex workers are charismatic leaders who can charm you or quickly have you bent double laughing. They have a wicked sense of humour, and they party hard. Theirs is a tough life, and that attitude towards the outside world is one of their ways of coping. They truly live for the day.

Sex workers are selfless

Avahan over time became a women's movement, with thousands of sex workers, often fierce competitors for clients, putting their individual interests aside to come together in common cause – the rights of their community. Part 2 of this narrative describes in more detail how that movement was built. Here I want to highlight one very personal aspect of sex workers' selflessness – their love for their children.

No woman wants to get into sex work. It's not that they made a choice, but rather that they had no choice to make. Their life is tough, but sex workers so often just live to create a better future for their kids. It is the single overriding reason why they carry on.

If you meet a sex worker, it is quite likely that there will be a little kid, probably under six, somewhere close by. I've often found sex workers' children incredibly cute. They rollick and play in brothel corridors, disappear under their mother's bed and keep very quiet, when told to. They have all the needs – for stories, toys, playmates – that any small child has. Their mothers try their best to provide a life as 'normal' as possible for them.

I have put this question to sex workers all over India: What do you want for your child? If the child is a girl, almost unanimously, they say they don't want their children to become sex workers. They are driven by the belief that their kids will do well in school, go to college, get a steady job – everything any mother would want, and more. So often I found that their biggest fear is not HIV, but the prospect of dying before their children have grown up.

I've seen sex workers in their thirties and forties who have a daughter in university in the big city. I've seen cases where the kids, when old enough to know, are proud of the sacrifices their mothers made to give them a good life. In some rare cases the mother would say she successfully hid her profession from her daughter all through. But often, fate does not allow for a happy ending. The truth is that some children do get trafficked. But for the most part, I am convinced that sex workers are as good as the best mothers in the world.

The selflessness of the sex worker for her child is a deeply personal thing. Their selflessness in the service of their community is another thing altogether. We will come back to this.

~

One of my colleagues told me once that she was talking to a sex worker about her life when the woman snapped her fingers and said quietly: 'That's all it takes. You could have been sitting in my place, and I in yours.' If life had dealt them better cards, they could have been leaders somewhere else, in another India.

My friends would ask the same question. 'Why are you doing this stuff, Ashok? Doesn't it get you down?' The answer, one that I rarely articulated, was that I was constantly learning about life, leadership, and values from the commercial sex worker. That's what made it such a great journey.

7

Heartbreak in Eden

'You begin experiencing the rush even as the needle is in the vein. It rushes up your spine and explodes in your brain, your mouth falls open, and the high escapes from there with a sound.'

The other users nodded and laughed at the vivid description by Joey the peer worker. I wasn't sure if he was pulling my leg. Early into Avahan, I was with Joey and his friends in Imphal – the capital of Manipur, which was in the grip of an HIV epidemic driven by injecting drug use. It was dangerous territory because the Indian army was effectively at war with an entrenched underground insurgency movement. A friend from Manipur gave me a helpful suggestion before we left Delhi. 'When you come out of the airport, you will hit a T-point. Make sure you turn right – the road will lead you to the city.' When I asked the obvious question, he said, 'Don't turn left – you may get shot.' I laughed, but soon realized he was deadly serious.

That trip to Imphal was the first of many journeys I was to make to our two programme states in the remote North-East – Manipur and neighbouring Nagaland, small states with a combined population of just over four million. The region is connected to the rest of India by the Siliguri Corridor (also known as the 'chicken's neck'), a narrow strip of land only twenty-three kilometres across. It was a place that India seemed to have forgotten, and travelling across Manipur and Nagaland was sometimes like being transported to a dreamlike land. Here I found serene natural beauty, and warm, gifted people, experiencing a heartache that had become part of their daily life – the ongoing tragedy of guns, drugs, needles, and, inevitably, HIV.

∼

Manipur and Nagaland have each had a long history of violent armed conflict. That conflict continues to this day and – if one were to simplify a highly complex situation – essentially has three strands. There is the struggle for an independent greater Nagaland; the war between two ethnic groups, the Meiteis and the Nagas in Manipur; and the never-ending internecine clashes between tribes in both states.

The Nagas are the hill people and are to be found across many states in the North-East, and into western Myanmar. Well before India's independence in 1947, the Nagas, led by Angami Zapu Phizo, had been demanding a unified greater Nagaland, linking Naga peoples all the way up to Assam. By the 1950s, this had turned into an armed struggle against 'India', with various militant underground groups pitted against the Indian army. That fight has persisted for decades and it was always a backdrop to our work in Nagaland and Manipur. Today there is a peace accord in place, which ensures relative calm.

In Manipur the major conflict is between the Meiteis and the Nagas. The Meiteis are the valley people located around Imphal. They comprise 65 per cent of the population, but are relegated to only 10 per cent of the land. That is the core of their conflict – the Meiteis wanting to expand into the hills and the Nagas seeking to protect their lands.

Among the Nagas there are about twenty distinct tribes, engaged in recurring internecine clashes, often savage in nature, and over seemingly small disputes. In Manipur there are also encounters between Nagas and Kukis, the other major ethnic group.

∼

It is always useful to understand history, but for us the bottom line was that violent conflict, a way of life in both Manipur and Nagaland, had a direct bearing on the twin epidemics of drug use and HIV. In the years we were working in the North-East, there were several militant underground groups, called 'UGs' by local people. The common enemy for all the UGs was the Indian army, which was out in force in Manipur and Nagaland. The controversial Armed Forces Special Protection Act (AFSPA) gave the army sweeping powers – for instance, to arrest without showing cause – and it had been misused on several occasions.[1] As we drove through the interiors of Manipur, we would sometimes see long military convoys, minesweepers being deployed, soldiers in full combat armour combing the inner roads.

The biggest casualty in all this were the youth, who had no outlets for fun or work. Youngsters could not go and watch a movie because the UGs had banned films 'from India'. Manipur has such varied and delightful regional cuisine, but there were no proper restaurants in Imphal. The most coveted of jobs was virtually any position in government – the pay was low, but at least it meant lifetime employment. But there were very few job opportunities in, or outside, government. All this was fertile ground for guns and needles.

Mothers, it was said, would hide their teenaged sons when the UGs came along to recruit. However, many a young man willingly chose to go that way. The attraction of a gun in hand, the respect he thought would come with that, was better than any alternative he had before him. And if he didn't join the militants, the young man might well take to drugs and fall victim to the HIV virus.

~

The HIV epidemic was raging in Manipur and Nagaland. As late as 2007, several districts in these states had the highest HIV levels in India, such as Ukhrul (6 per cent) in Manipur, and Tuensang (5.6 per cent) in Nagaland.[2] Data on prevalence among injecting drug users was unreliable, but was reportedly as high as 17 per cent in Manipur.

Two drugs were in vogue, Spasmo Proxyvon (SP) and heroin. SP is a common muscle relaxant and painkiller that comes in tablet form. It is harmless if taken orally in the prescribed quantity. However, drug users had discovered that if injected, it gave an instantaneous rush, which users like Joey found was even more powerful than that from heroin. SP tablets were dissolved in a few tablespoons of boiled water and the suspension injected into a vein. SP was used mainly by the younger addicts because it was cheap: a strip of ten tablets cost less than a hundred rupees. Because the drug was not meant to be injected, it created abscesses. The addict's hands and legs were often covered with sores, and he would have to inject directly into the boil because he couldn't find a vein.

For injecting drug users who could afford it, there was always the luxury of a heroin fix. Heroin came in four grades, of which '#4', also known as 'China White', was the purest grade, freely available in Manipur and Nagaland. In 2004 it cost only eight hundred rupees for a gram of #4 in Moreh, the Manipur town at the border with Myanmar which is the entry point for the drug. That gram would cost ten to twelve times that amount in Delhi and at least thirty times the Moreh price on the streets of New York.

Pure grade heroin was easily available in the region due to its proximity to the Golden Triangle, an area of approximately 9,50,000 square kilometres that cuts across the mountains of three Southeast Asian countries: Myanmar, Laos, and Thailand. Heroin made in factories in these countries – illegally or in some cases with the government looking away – would be smuggled through Moreh into Manipur, and then on to Delhi and other big cities and to Europe and all the way to the United States. Manipur and Nagaland were the very first stops on this route.

~

Injecting drug users would often share a single needle, because needles were not easily available, and for the feeling of fellowship that comes from shooting up together. As needles got shared, a tiny amount of whole blood would often get transferred with the syringe from one addict to the other. That transfer was more likely if the injection had been into an abscess, because a vein could not be found. Whole blood exchange is the most rapid form of HIV transmission with a more than ten times greater risk of transmission in a single exchange with an infected partner.

HIV prevention with injecting drug user populations happens through a protocol called 'harm reduction'. As relapse rates are high with heroin addiction, the primary goal is to reduce the harm an addict can do to himself and thereby, from a public health viewpoint, reduce HIV transmission in the population. There are two components to harm reduction: needle exchange and opioid substitution therapy (OST). With needle exchange, the addict is given fresh needles equal to the number of needles he turns in. This practice was pioneered in Amsterdam in 1984 and in Merseyside (UK) in 1986. The first large-scale OST programme, the methadone maintenance treatment (MMT) programme, was adopted in Germany in 1987.

In OST the addict is provided with an opioid substitute for the injected drug, under careful medical supervision. Because the opioid is taken under the tongue, it eliminates the needle-transmission route for HIV, and the risk of transmission from whole blood exchange.

Two drugs are used in OST: buprenorphine and methadone. Both provide the euphoric effects of heroin, but without as strong a rush. They have a long half-life (the period taken to reach maximum effect), which could be as much as two to three days with a single dose, eliminating the sudden peaks and lows and therefore the greater number of fixes needed with heroin. Weaning the addict from opioid substitutes has a much higher success rate. Both drugs are effective, and each has its advantages, limitations, and associated controversies. Ideally a programme should allow for both, so a switchover is possible where indicated. NACO allowed for buprenorphine, but not methadone, in the national AIDS programmes. As late as 2006, OST was not widespread in the North-East.

NACO's harm reduction policy was an enlightened one, considering that several developed countries did not allow the use of government funds for needle exchange programmes and sometimes OST as well.[3] The conservative view in those countries was that harm reduction only helped an addict to stay addicted. This, even though harm reduction is endorsed by the World Health Organization.

~

The alternatives are grim. My first exposure to 'cold turkey' de-addiction as it was being practised in the North-East was chilling. I was in Churachandpur, a town with a population of about 2,70,000, in the south-west of Manipur, about sixty kilometres south of Imphal. I was at the wonderful needle exchange project managed by the NGO Shalom. 'At present there are thirteen private rehabs in Churachandpur, including three where chains are used,' the head of the NGO, Dr Moina, told us. Here, the addict is chained to a bed and locked in a dark room to suffer the agonies of withdrawal, sometimes with only a Bible as companion.

We visited one such rehab centre, a small, innocuous house painted a bright white. 'This rehab centre practises chaining for a period up to three years,' the Shalom worker told us. The couple who owned the house were devout Christians. They denied that any form of coercion was practised in their rehab – only good nourishment and Bible studies. They met us at the picket fence that ran around the house. They were polite, but did not invite us in.

I was troubled to hear about the chaining. The Shalom worker said, 'This is not as cruel as it may sound. The drug problem is so bad in Churachandpur that parents are known to bribe their kids' way into jail, because they have no hope of his surviving on the outside. Think of this rehab as just another form of jail.'

I spoke to the peer worker Joey, an addict who had been 'sent' to jail by his parents. 'The problem is that parents don't know about the torture you go through with withdrawal. In any case, every drug possible was available in jail, only needles were rare,' Joey told me. 'At one time only two or three needles were being circulated among four to five hundred users in Imphal jail. People had heard about HIV, but that didn't stop anyone. Once you are going through the pains of withdrawal nothing is important except the next fix.' Recounting his time in Imphal jail, Joey said that HIV was rampant. Indeed, in a study done in Imphal jail in 1993, 80 per cent of the inmates were found to be HIV positive.[4]

When I was invited to deliver the Gustav Nossal Oration at the University of Melbourne in 2006, I took the opportunity to visit one of the several outpatient de-addiction centres in the city. In a brightly lit, cheerful clinic, heroin addicts read magazines, watched TV, and patiently awaited their daily dose of methadone or buprenorphine, a sky-blue liquid, which they readily swallowed and then left. I spoke to a few, who told me that it had been a smooth transition from injecting to the oral drug. How different this state-of-the-art harm reduction programme was from the chains and Bible protocol being practised out of sheer desperation in the North-East!

~

On one of our first trips to Nagaland, we landed in Dimapur, a dusty town in the plains, after a five-hour journey by air from Delhi. We were met by Sunny Meitei, a former major in India's commando Special Forces and head of our security team. We always used security when we travelled in the North-East. We held short meetings with NGOs such as Bethesda, Akimbo, and Prodigals Home, working with injecting drug users and sex workers.

After an early lunch we set off for our destination, Kohima, the state capital, a town set at an elevation of 1400 metres. As we climbed the narrow hill roads, the land shyly revealed its lush green beauty. The road had many twists and turns and at every major bend there was a road sign with some pithy advice: 'Driving Whisky, Really Risky' and 'Don't Gossip, He's Driving'. One I particularly liked, after a sharp speed breaker, simply said, 'We Warned You'. We stopped to eat pineapples on the roadside at ten rupees each. Small, with a tangy-honey taste, they were heavenly. I packed a few to take back home, assured by the vendor that they would grow splendidly in Delhi. Of course, they had dried up by the time I reached home.

Our first glimpse of Kohima was enchanting. Coming around a bend in the mountain road, we saw a pretty town of small houses spread across two hills shrouded in mist. We checked into our hotel to freshen up before the launch ceremony of Orchid, our programme in the North-East. Orchid was led by Dr Biangtung Langkham, who had vast experience working with injecting drug users and HIV in the region.

I was glad I'd carried a blazer and tie because the Governor, chief minister, and most of the cabinet were there, all dressed formally. It was a stirring ceremony at which the government conveyed how much they appreciated our help and expressed their strong commitment and support.

That evening, the local NGO laid out a captivating cultural programme, the highlight of which was a classical dance performance by eight members of the Numi Pambi community. The name literally means 'like a woman', and it was apt, because the men indeed looked like flawlessly beautiful young women. They are regarded as artists by the public because of the central role of the woman that they play in 'Sumang Lila', traditional street drama. I went up onstage at the end to receive the traditional red-and-black Manipuri woollen shawl given to guests. The Numi Pambis had their eyes cast down. They spoke shyly when I appreciated their performance and asked about their art. They came across in every way as poised, demure young women.

The Numi Pambis are men who have sex with men, and some of them are also commercial sex workers. Their acceptance by society is part of the more open social norms that prevail in Manipur and Nagaland.

∼

The next day we took time out from work to visit the Kohima war memorial. It was hard to imagine that this serene town had been the site of one of the most important battles of the Second World War. The Japanese 31st Division, approaching India through Burma, had reached Kohima in 1944, to confront the vastly outnumbered Second British Division, which included many British regiments as well as the Indian Assam Regiment. The Indians were the first to confront the Japanese, as a front line at Jessami, fifty-five kilometres from Kohima, and fell fighting. At Kohima a pitched battle ensued, its final stages fought almost hand to hand, across the lines of the tennis court at the deputy commissioner's residence. Today those lines are marked in concrete, and the site is a war memorial maintained by the Commonwealth War Graves Commission. Descendants of the 2337 soldiers buried here – British, Indian, and Japanese – come every year to pay their respects. If they had won, the Japanese would have continued their march into India.

At the entrance to the memorial are engraved the poignant words 'When you go home, tell them of us and say – for your tomorrow, we gave our today.'

~

Orchid did some exceptional advocacy work to ensure that the UGs did not interfere with our work, either in Nagaland or in Manipur. This was not a minor task, considering that almost everyone, NGOs included, had to give a cut of 15–25 per cent of their funds to the UGs.

The advocacy was a concerted and savvy campaign led by Orchid's quietly charismatic leader, Langkham. He was a medical doctor brought up in a small village three days' walk from Churachandpur. Just about five feet tall, with a gentle, almost apologetic voice, an Ordained Elder of the Manipur Baptist Church, Langkham could easily be underestimated. But underneath this was a person with a steely resolve, relentless when he wanted something for the greater good of Orchid. When Langkham started working with Avahan, he asked me how much I wanted to know about how he dealt with the 'powers that be' in the North-East. 'Only as much as I need to know,' I replied just as cryptically, but I made it clear we could not pay. It was a good arrangement.

Langkham's first level of advocacy was with people who were widely admired and respected by the UGs, such as university professors and retired judges. Langkham decided that that was not enough. Crucially, he once managed to arrange safe passage to meet with the supreme leader of the UGs. The legendary Thuingaleng Muivah, wanted in India, lived in Thailand and had come to Delhi, given safe passage for peace talks with the Indian government. He was reported to be somewhere in Nagaland, and Langkham had somehow secured a meeting with the UG's leadership cadre deep in the jungle. This may be one of the things that Langkham thought I didn't need to know in advance!

He was accompanied by Beth Fuller, thirty-five, a programme management specialist from Melbourne, who was leading Orchid's technical work, living and working in the region.

Beth says: 'It was a long drive and, having entered thick forest, we were driven on dirt roads, passing through several checkpoints armed by soldiers with machine guns, dressed in battle fatigues. At the camp, there were heavily armed soldiers everywhere. We were taken into a large meeting room, where about a hundred people, including the full "parliament" of the UGs, had gathered. There were ministers there in charge of different areas – home, finance, and so on. I gave a PowerPoint presentation that lasted about an hour. We explained the epidemic, how it was spreading and affecting the population, how it might wreck society, and what we are trying to do.

'Muivah listened attentively and asked some questions. They were all very polite. At the end he said words I'll never forget: "We love our cause dearly, but you love your cause even more. Your work is even more noble than ours." He guaranteed that the Orchid programme would never be harassed, and said he should be contacted if we ever faced any problems.'

Beth continues: 'I went away so inspired. A year later my husband, John, and I left for Australia. Our baby was born in Melbourne soon after. We named him Kohima. He is fifteen now, and one day plans to go and see the places we have spoken so much about, with him.'

~

The 140-kilometre segment of NH2 that connects Kohima to Imphal is a silent highway, weaving its way through the clouds. Small villages suddenly appear along the way, with little shacks selling pineapples, oranges, and peaches. Fresh orchids, plentiful in the state, are also on sale. Elderly men sipped steaming tea, sitting on creaky chairs, and watched with mild interest when we stopped to stretch our legs. 'What's changed here since you were a young man, pabung?' I ask one of them, using the respectful term for elder. 'Nothing has changed, everything is just the same,' he says. After thinking a bit, he adds, 'Maybe there are better cars that drive by on the road from Kohima.' Indeed, time seems to have stood still in this distant part of India.

Over the course of several visits we made across Nagaland and Manipur, we covered most of the twenty districts in the two states. My colleague Hari Menon and I once arrived in the tiny village-town of Pfutsero in Nagaland, high up on one of the hills. After a long, climbing drive, we were both ravenous. The locals had laid out lunch on a long table, next to which was a much smaller one that had two covered dishes. They explained that as per tradition those dishes were specialities of the region reserved for the most honoured guests – which in this case were Hari and I. Hari is an adventurer when it comes to new foods and I am more conservative. The specialities were fried hornets and oak tree maggot, both cooked in local sauces. To refuse would be to insult the hosts. While Hari jumped in, I approached the table warily. I need not have worried – it was altogether delicious and nothing was wasted.

Another memory is of Moreh, a remote, lawless Wild West–style town in south Manipur, bordering Myanmar. We simply stepped over the border, after a government official laconically stamped a twelve-hour visa form. A strange trade exchange was in progress – a line of Burmese sex workers crossing into Manipur, almost rubbing shoulders with IDUs from Manipur going into Myanmar. We spent time in Churachandpur, Ukhrul, and Chandel, and many other charming towns, all ravaged by HIV and insurgency.

Each of us on the Avahan team who got a chance to work and travel extensively in Manipur and Nagaland carries vivid memories of our times there – of the varied and beautiful landscape, the hospitality and warmth of the people, and the distinctive local cuisines. But our lasting impression is of sadness and despair, and enduring heartbreak.

~

We visited several model injecting drug user programmes that Project Orchid was funding in Manipur, such as those run by Shalom and Sahara in Churachandpur and Raikizumi in Pfutsero. At one of these, we met Moya, a young man of about eighteen. Moya was a peer worker – a former injecting drug user – whose job was to ensure that addicts are brought into the programme and use clean needles. Moya, with other peers, ran a management information system that tracked every individual drug user in their programme territory. Avahan, throughout our six states, was emphasizing individual-level data tracking. Each peer kept a register that carefully recorded needles given and returned for each injecting user. If Moya gave an addict five needles, he would expect those back on a fixed date, and he would then give him five new needles. If the drug user did not come back, Moya would go out to find him. Needle exchange was vitally important because substitution therapy was almost non-existent at that time.

Moya wore tight, faded jeans, and a bright orange round-necked T-shirt. There was a chain of black and red beads on his left wrist, and a pair of dilapidated loafers on his feet. Moya was gently charismatic, speaking so softly that I had to lean forward to make out what he was saying. He was ashamed to say he was an ex-user and introduced himself as an artist. He remained a good football player, who had been invited for trials by a Delhi football league. 'I'd like to go, but I can't, I've stuff to look after here,' he said. After a pause he asked, 'Would you like to meet one of the users? There's someone just come in to exchange his needles.'

I was in for a shock. The drug addict he spoke of was plump and apple-cheeked and seemed about twelve years old. 'He's actually about sixteen,' said Moya when he saw my surprised look. 'There are lots of kids like him, but not many who participate in the exchange programme. We have even had mothers come to trade their kids' needles. They tell me they warn their kids not to share the needles with their friends in school.'

The Orchid programme depended on peer workers like Moya, ex-users who knew the injecting drug user community intimately. It was not an easy job. 'I'm sometimes roughed up by the UGs, when I'm only trying to do my job', he told me.

~

The UGs exercised a peculiar morality. They were against drugs and believed that only harsh measures could curb usage. They followed a quaint etiquette. Any addict they caught using would receive a beating, the first time. The next time he was caught, he would be shot, a flesh wound through the calf that would not touch the bone. Drug peddlers, if caught, were often shot and killed on the spot. This practice had absolutely no impact on the epidemic. Injecting drug use continued unabated.

One day, as I sat in my office in Delhi, I got a call from Langkham. 'I have some bad news,' he said. 'One of our peer workers has been shot by the UGs, but don't worry, it's only a flesh wound.' My heart sank. I imagined that when word got back to the foundation in Seattle that an Avahan worker had been shot in the line of duty, they would shut down Orchid.

Langkham told me he would send me some pictures. I wasn't sure what I was to do after seeing the photographs, and I wasn't looking forward to it. They arrived within a few hours. What struck me was the almost surgical precision with which the shooting had been done. There were two neat puncture holes, about a half-centimetre in diameter and about an inch apart. The bullet in each case had gone right through the flesh and emerged, leaving another two holes where they had come out. I showed the pictures to Sunny Meitei, who glanced at them and confirmed this was a ritual warning, intended to scare, but not maim.

I asked Langkham to do a thorough investigation into the shooting, and he reported back in a few days. What he told me was a relief: the shooting had nothing whatsoever to do with the programme. The peer had been shot as part of a local dispute. I would of course never know the full truth, but I reported the whole matter to the foundation. They were very understanding, and Orchid continued to do its life-saving work.

~

Perhaps the most stigmatized of groups were the 'IDU widows', women whose husbands had died of an overdose or because of HIV. Almost every family in Manipur and Nagaland had been affected by injecting drug use, directly or indirectly. These widows were often left destitute and some had turned to sex work to feed their families. In Churachandpur, we climbed a rickety flight of steps to visit Shalom's one-room community centre for sex workers, mainly IDU widows. The sex workers received the same services that Avahan provided in other states: counselling, regular STI check-ups, and condoms. Unlike sex workers in other parts of India, these women were too shy to talk to men who were strangers, so I waited outside while the women in our team talked to them.

One woman came out of the room, and I introduced myself cautiously. Roslyn would have been about thirty-five but looked about fifty years old. She said she had been widowed three years ago. She had taken to sex work soon after to look after her three small children – aged four, nine, and eleven. Clearly, it was difficult to be an IDU wife and mother in Manipur, and the experience had prematurely aged Roslyn.

Later on in that visit, I was in Bishnupur, a town of about 9500 people due south of Imphal, named after its ancient Vishnu temple. The NGO had arranged for me to meet with six IDU widows who had become sex workers. They were all in their early twenties. Each spoke of the stigma they faced after their husbands had died. It was as though the stigma had a life of its own. It had the drug user in its grip when he was alive, and for now did not bother his wife. When he died, it immediately seized his widow. Many women told me that as a result they had no alternative but to 'sell vegetables in the market', a euphemism for turning to sex work.

~

Vijay Chibber was an IAS officer and finance secretary in Manipur when I started my visits to the state. We had studied together at St Stephen's College in Delhi, and I was meeting him after many years. Vijay invited me over to his place for drinks when I called and announced that I was in Manipur. I'd read that he had survived a violent assassination attempt by the UGs, and I wanted to learn how the underground movement continued to thrive. Vijay poured me a Scotch, and I settled down to be educated. I started by asking about the assassination attempt.

'You must understand that it is the UGs who rule Manipur,' he said. 'They take 15 per cent as protection money from every single transaction that happens in the state. Every shopkeeper pays this percentage of his income, as does almost every cop. If you cooperate, they won't harm you, and you can live within the system.' It occurred to me then that we had worked without obstruction from the UGs so far in Manipur.

'Yes, they tried to assassinate me – in my own office. I saw the gun coming in through the skylight, and on instinct I ducked under the desk – but two of my staff got killed. I don't bear any ill will towards the UGs for this attack – they were doing their job, and I had made it clear I would do mine. They have their own code of honour. They will never shoot you straight out, they will warn you three times first, by letter. The third time I was warned, the person appealed to me not to get myself killed needlessly.'

Vijay continued: 'When someone in government does not cooperate they pick them up politely from their homes and take them into the forest. There, they offer a cup of tea and gently tell you why they need cooperation. For each major government position, they have their shadow counterparts.'

I had my own frightening experience of the war zone later that evening. After dinner, some fine Manipuri pork curry with rice, Vijay said he would drop me at my hotel. I was looking forward to my comfortable bed in my favourite Room 506, at the Nirmala, the only decent hotel in town. Vijay dropped me off at the road across from the Nirmala and sped off – I hoped he'd be safe driving, both of us having finished half the fine bottle of Scotch he had opened before dinner.

When I went up to the Nirmala I found that the shutters were down, padlocked at ground level from the outside. I knocked on the metal shutters, banged, then kicked, with increasing urgency. There was not a sound, and not a soul on the streets to help. When I looked around, I noticed for the first time that every shop was shuttered and no room had a light on anywhere. My phone battery had died, I saw with a shock. I began imagining being picked up by the UGs. I was beginning to regret having persuaded security that I didn't need them that evening. I was getting panicky and started thinking of a hidden corner to pass the night in.

At that moment Vijay's car screeched to a stop – only two minutes may have passed since he left me, but it had seemed an eternity. 'Sorry about that, Choki. I forgot entirely that the shutters would be down. There's no way anyone will open, they will assume we are UGs. Let's go home.'

~

In March 2003, just as we started our trips to the North-East, a German national working for a local NGO was kidnapped by rebels of the Kuki Liberation Army from a village near Imphal. He was released unharmed after three weeks. Somehow, we never felt the least bit nervous, though Gates Foundation staff would no doubt have been a good catch for the UGs.

I once asked Sunny Meitei, 'Would it be a good idea to travel as part of an army convoy in certain places?' It was a naive question, and he just smiled and told me that travelling with the army was probably the most dangerous thing we could do in the North-East. He added, 'Perhaps the safest thing would be to have an old Manipuri or Naga lady as part of your team and have her in the car whenever you travel.' It was a serious suggestion. Elderly women, especially mothers, were held in deep respect. No one would raise a finger on a group that had a grandmother in it.

Indeed, there was a Mothers' Association that wielded a lot of power. The church also had considerable influence in the two states, which had a large Christian population, mainly Protestant – 90 per cent in Nagaland and 34 per cent in Manipur. For various reasons, we did not work with the mothers or the church. They both did splendid work with the injecting drug users in their own ways. But somewhere, the moral aspect of drugs came into their approach, and we did not think morality could tackle HIV, either with drug users or with sex workers.

Once we were in Imphal and needed to get to Chandel, seventy-five kilometres away. Chandel was considered a breeding ground for insurgents but it was also an important place for us to visit from our work viewpoint. Sunny had his contacts with the UGs – we never asked about these – and he had been assured safe passage. He said he would never consider doing anything that was even remotely risky, but as per the routine, he would have to run it by the foundation's security team in Seattle. He had bulletproof vests for me and the two Aparajitas on my team (Ramakrishnan and Bhalla – we called them AR and AB). This, he said, was just a precaution in case of being caught in a crossfire. It all sounded fine, and I was keen to get to Chandel.

AB had joined Avahan just the week before, and this was her first field trip. She says, 'When I opened the door to my room and saw a bulletproof vest laid out neatly on the bed, I was mightily scared, and wondered what kind of job I had taken. I didn't tell my husband after I got home.'

However, our security team in Seattle said a firm no to the drive to Chandel, and Sunny told me the trip was being called off. I spoke to security myself, but they told me if this was to be approved they would have to refer it upwards, which meant it would go up to the president of global health. Frustrated, we dropped what promised to have been an exciting trip.

~

Work in the North-East was especially draining, physically and emotionally, for those of my colleagues who spent more time there, such as Aparajita Ramakrishnan and Sema Sgaier. Aparajita oversaw our North-East programme for a few years, and she struggled to control her emotions as she related an incident that shook her:

'We were in Ukhrul in Manipur, when we came across a girl called Likevi. She was thirteen, HIV positive, and being looked after by her nine-year-old sister. They were living with their grandparents, both parents having died of HIV. The father had been an addict, and the mother got HIV from him. Some NGO staff approached us before we left, asking urgently that we take Likevi to the general hospital in Imphal. Likevi was sick and needed urgent attention.

'The girl was wasted, bones so bare that each knock as the car hit the road caused her excruciating pain, because there was no fat left on her, only nerves. I cradled her head on my lap. The car ride to the Jawaharlal Nehru Hospital in Imphal was pure torture for Likevi and she screamed in pain all the way. At the hospital she threw herself off the bed, in what looked like an attempt to end it all.

'I got the news of Likevi's dying when I was back in Delhi, a day after we admitted her. I wept for days. At that time, I thought I could not go on with Avahan, that the work was too cruel, and that I should quit.'

~

Twelve years after I first met Joey, the heroin addict whose parents had 'sent' him to jail, I met him again for this book, curious to know his life story and how he was doing since we last met. Growing up in Imphal, Joey had been an A-grade student, a state-level sportsman. His father worked in the railways and was always away on different postings. Joey's route to shooting heroin began innocuously, with a popular codeine-based cough mixture, Phensedyl. In eighth grade he and his friends found that the syrup could give a lasting kick if they drank a small bottle. Entrepreneurial chemists sold it to them at five times the price.

Gulping cough mixture soon led to smoking heroin, pure #4 straight from Myanmar through the border town of Moreh. Sliding grades, dropping out from life, recovery with good resolutions, relapse again – fifteen years went by this way, in the grip of heroin. Joey recovered again, for over a year. He swore that this time it was forever, and he was accepted by Orchid. He became a master trainer, an expert on methadone treatment, attending conferences abroad, and was widely sought.

Joey was clean for eight years till one day, by chance, he met an old friend who asked him if he wanted some heroin, and the word inexplicably came out from his lips, 'Yes.' He still doesn't know why.

There wasn't enough drug to inhale, and Joey had never injected till then, so his friend shot him up. He stayed injecting and undetected at work, using his expert knowledge of methadone to shoot and withdraw in cycles, for two years. In November 2017 he came clean again, and continues serving others, as a senior manager at a well-known NGO in Bangalore. He owes his recovery to his wife, he says.

Joey's story speaks of the icy, vice-like grip of hard drugs, and his honesty, courage, and will to survive. This time, he says, it really is quits.

~

At dinner in Kohima one evening, I was unable to place the nationality of a young NGO worker who wore Western clothes and had an accent that seemed foreign. 'Are you from India?' I asked. 'I am Naga,' she replied pointedly. I asked her if she would want to use her rich experience to work on the larger epidemic in other parts of India, after she returned from a brief assignment abroad. Her answer was forthright: 'I will always be happy serving the Naga people – and if not, then that of the North-East.'

The people I met in Nagaland and Manipur routinely used the phrase 'came from India'. They considered India a foreign country, a neighbour who cared little for their welfare. And why not? Here was a region of unspoiled beauty, inhabited by hospitable people. 'India' had allowed this Eden to be ravaged by an insurgency fundamentally born out of a lack of development investment.

Manipur, for example, is a tourist's delight. It is a tiny state of green valleys and hills, where wild orchids bloom freely. The climate is moderate through most of the year. Potential tourist attractions abound. There is Moirang, where the Indian National Army flag was hoisted in 1944; the huge freshwater lake Loktak with its floating islands of cultivation, the biggest in the North-East; the Siroi Hills, where the exquisite Siroi lily grows; the Sanghai deer unique to Manipur; and much more. The cultures of the several tribes and communities is each uniquely special, and the range of cuisines amazing.

~

I was asked more than once by people in the HIV sector why we chose to work in the North-East. Their logic was that the states are tiny, and almost cut off from the mainland, and therefore they could only have marginal impact on the larger 'Indian' epidemic. Programme spending is always a trade-off, and the real question was, couldn't the same money be deployed elsewhere? It was a question that needed to be asked, but somewhere it infuriated me because it was inevitably asked by people who had spent no time in the North-East and witnessed its heartbreak. For us, Manipur and Nagaland went beyond the sometimes heartless rationale of HIV transmission epidemiology. I insisted that they be treated as integral parts of Avahan.

Having said that, we had no illusions that there was a near-term solution. The fundamental problems were to do with the system itself – lack of opportunity, free availability of drugs, tribal enmity, a war zone. It seemed only economic development could sort things out, and the government seemed apathetic to the plight of the entire region. Perhaps the best we could do was to reduce harm and hope that it would make a big difference.

Langkham says, 'Over the course of Avahan, people most at risk to HIV, the injecting drug users, found that they could raise their voices and be heard. Today, awareness is much higher, and needle exchange is widely accepted. But in a fundamental way, nothing much has changed. Job opportunities are few, the UGs are still there. It is a half-won battle.'

Adult HIV prevalence in the North-East is still a cause for concern, with three states having the highest levels of adult HIV prevalence – Manipur at 1.15 per cent, and Nagaland and Mizoram at 0.8 per cent, according to NACO.

8

Seeking Nirvana

In a dimly lit room in Coimbatore, a bustling city in southern Tamil Nadu, six transgenders, aravani pengal as they were known, squatted on the ground with their guru Selvi, who had a bristly square jaw, and huge, adamant breasts. One minute the aravanis had been rolling in laughter, one bawdy tale following another, but the next moment, at a signal from Selvi, there was a hushed silence. The ceremony to adopt Hari Menon and me as brothers was about to begin. It was a rare honour being bestowed on us, signifying that they trusted us implicitly.

Selvi led an energetic group chanting, punctuated by raucous cries as the names of each person in their line of gurus was invoked. Sweet-pungent incense filled the air, a drum was beaten, and hands clapped with a loud retort, using the method of slap-rotating the palms together, the distinctive way of transgender people. Hari and I sat cross-legged before Selvi, hands folded and heads bowed. When the short ceremony ended, we rose and Selvi gave each of us a gift of a shirt piece and 205 rupees. We bent and touched her feet, and she blessed us with a palm held over our heads. The blessings of an aravani mean a lot, and we left deeply moved.

That ceremony was but one curious episode in a journey that took me into the shadow world of those groups so highly at risk of contracting the HIV virus – the kothis, panthis, double-deckers, and aquas, all seeking a special sort of Nirvana.

~

The typologies of 'male with male' sex in the invisible India are complex. Individuals and communities present themselves as though from inside a kaleidoscope, changing with every shake. They blend into each other, defying convenient categorizations, such as gay or drag queen. The only thing in common among them is the desperate circumstances in which they live.

These are hidden communities, even more so than the female sex workers or the injecting drug users. They shared with me customs and traditions that few outsiders are privy to. Their activities were stigmatized, and even illegal at that time. Respecting that confidentiality, I provide only enough information for the reader to appreciate their circumstances. Perhaps the best way to start is to put on my old McKinsey hat and attempt a systematic way of classifying different typologies of MSM – men who have sex with men – and transgenders.

Why is the term MSM rather than gay used in the HIV sector? It is an umbrella term that connotes a wide variety of male to male sexual relationships. For example, the swarthy sardar trucker who has sex regularly with the teenage 'helper' who travels with him could well seize you by the throat if you called him gay. He has sex more often with women, and his self-image is that of a macho man. The term transgender, or TG for short, is also an umbrella word in which is contained a gamut of typologies. The broad classes of MSM and TG also blend into each other.

This is how I sorted through these sexual identities. The kothi is the man who is at the receiving end of anal sex. The kothi will rarely take on the role of the penetrator, and he may be married with children – often as a cover for his secret life. Our programme worked almost entirely with kothi MSMs. They are also of different types. A kothi may present himself as a regular masculine individual, sometimes putting on feminine mannerisms. On the other hand, a 'sathla' kothi is an effeminate cross-dresser. For example, he may go to college dressed as a man, and don a sari when with friends, or cruising.

The panthi is one who plays the male role. He may be a penetrator only of men, or he may also penetrate women. The double-decker (DD) plays both roles, giver and receiver. He may transact only with men, or with both men and women. Some, but not all, kothis, DDs, and TGs are commercial sex workers, sometimes dedicated to a few lovers, or having multiple partners. They may have 'married' relationships with the same sex, or they may be free cruisers.

~

The Netherlands, in 2001, became the first country to allow same-sex marriage. Following that enlightened example, several countries including the United Kingdom, Canada, the Scandinavian nations, Argentina, South Africa, and New Zealand also allowed same-sex marriage. Today in the United States, thirty states allow marriage licences to same-sex couples. Taiwan became the first country in Asia to legalize such unions.

While the world moved on, India (till September 2018) remained in the dark ages in its treatment of people who belong to lesbian, gay, bisexual, transgender and queer (LGBTQ) populations. Homosexuality was a criminal offence, punishable by up to eight years of rigorous imprisonment. This punishment was enforced by the notorious Section 377 of the Indian Penal Code, introduced by the British into Indian law back in 1860. More often it was a means for the police, or goons, to harass and extract a bribe from, for example, two young men innocently holding hands in a park.

In 2001, the Naz Foundation, led by Anjali Gopalan (the 'angel in disguise' mentioned in chapter 3), filed a lawsuit in the Delhi High Court seeking legalization of gay sex in India. In 2004, the litigation and a subsequent review petition were dismissed by the high court. In 2006, the Supreme Court directed the high court to reconsider the issue. Three years later when the high court in Delhi legalized gay sex among consenting adults on 2 July 2009, the MSM and transgender populations throughout India, and programmes like ours which worked with these communities, were elated.

Sadly, the huge positive impact this had on HIV prevention did not last. Subsequent counter-suits by religious organizations and politicians of various hues came up before the Supreme Court in 2012. With the Supreme Court setting aside the high court order from 2009, 11 December 2013 proved to be a Black Wednesday. This was overturned by a new bench of the highest court in 2018, hopefully forever.

~

As I came to know the community better, I realized that transgender people are really women, tragically trapped in a man's body. Selvi, for example, except for her ample bosom achieved through self-prescribed hormone consumption, had a stubble, square jaw, and broad shoulders. But she came across as a woman when you spoke to her.

What is it about Selvi and her aravani community that gives them a distinct identity, different from the gay men, cross-dressers, or stereotypical drag queens as they are characterized in the West? The answer is that Selvi is part of a cultural tradition, built around the belief that they are the spiritual brides of the god Aravan. That tradition is hundreds of years old in India and is preserved in an ethos that has prescribed norms of behaviour and arcane rituals.

There are over a hundred thousand transgenders in India, and they belong to one or the other of seven regionals 'gharanas'.[1] Examples are the Laskarwali gharana of Hyderabad, Bhendi Bazaar of Pune, and Lalankar of Mumbai. Each gharana is headed by an elderly naik who in turn has numerous 'naik chelas' – acolytes. The chelas themselves have several chelas of their own. The naik must have several leadership attributes such as influence skills, judgement, diplomacy, and patience.

Many naiks I've seen speak little and maintain a certain dignity. When a naik dies, there is a 'roti' – a meeting of all the naiks to select a successor, who is usually the late naik's lead chela. Aravanis usually belong to clusters known as jamaats, which could have ten to fifteen members, though these numbers vary widely. The jamaat is the clan-home of the aravani where, as in any family, there can be squabbles and even serious fights. The discipline of the jamaat, and the norms and rituals of the gharana, are safeguarded by the naik. These rituals may pertain to the welcoming of a new aravani into the jamaat, weddings, deaths and, as I experienced, even the adoption of brothers. The naik is a strong mother figure with a loving, protective relationship with her chelas. At its worst the relationship can be exploitative and abusive. The chela, I was told, is free to leave at any time – but she will have to pay the jamaat a 'dand' or penalty if she does.

Within this cultural tradition there may even be the well-educated and well-off aravanis. I have met engineers, university professors, and once a former investment banker from the aravani community. However, the majority of aravanis are utterly poor. Some were born into well-off families, but very often, at some stage, they would have been cast out to fend for themselves.

Unable to cope on her own, the aravani will seek out a jamaat that will accept her. She will go into one of three professions. The first is 'bhadai' – where aravanis show up in a small group with drums and bells to sing at weddings and births and to give their blessings in exchange for a negotiated remuneration. Put simply, they will create such a nuisance and embarrassment that the household hosting the celebration will pay them a few hundred rupees to just go away. No one will throw the aravanis out unpaid because it is believed that their blessings count – and it would be a bad omen to turn them away on a festive occasion.

The second profession is 'bhikhu' – begging for alms, typically at traffic signals. At the sight of a group of aravanis approaching with loud flat-slap clapping, drivers will hastily roll up their windows and lock their car doors. The more generous may give them a twenty-rupee note. The third profession, the one our programme was most involved with, is sex work.

There is one other differentiating factor between aravanis, and that is whether they are 'Aqua' or 'Nirvana'. A woman trapped in a man's body, living in Europe or America, may choose to undergo a sex change operation after professional counselling. A dirt-poor aravani in India may also want one – but she does not have the money or the access. She ends up choosing to get herself castrated – by a traditional dai or by one of the very few doctors in India who perform the operation. The emasculated one is known as Nirvana, the ones not emasculated as Aqua. I have met aravanis who suffered the terrible pain that follows the emasculation and are radiantly happy. I have heard of transgender persons who did not survive the dangerous procedure, and known others who despise the practice. Generally, the aravani who has achieved Nirvana gets a special respect within her jamaat, and likely a higher price if she is into commercial sex.

~

Transgender people in India are known by different names. In the north, the term used is hijra; in Tamil Nadu they are known as aravanis[2] and there is an important myth behind that name. In the Mahabharata, the god Aravan was the noble son of the mighty warrior Arjuna. Aravan valiantly offered himself as a human sacrifice so that the army of the good, the Pandavas, could achieve victory. He was a bachelor and asked Krishna for a single boon – that he may be married for one night. Krishna granted the wish, but no woman wanted to become a widow overnight. So Krishna assumed the form of Mohini, a beautiful goddess, and they lived together for a night, after which Aravan kept his pledge and was beheaded the next day. Therefore, the aravanis believe that they are married to Aravan in spirit. As Krishna was half-woman and half-man for that night, they too are of both sexes and have god in them. That is why the blessings of an aravani are valued.

Koovagam in Tamil Nadu is a sleepy village and the temple bells are silent, but for fifteen days a year it is a riot of colour and noise. My colleague Negar Akhavi and I travelled to this village two hundred kilometres from Chennai, to witness the unusual traditional wedding celebration spread over fifteen days and attended by several thousand transgenders from all over India, and even different parts of the world. At Koovagam, on one particular day, thousands of new entrants to the aravani tradition are ceremonially married to Aravan at the ancient Koothandavar temple.

The four-hour drive from Chennai by a good highway was a breeze, but two kilometres from the village, we slowed to a crawl. Wave upon wave of transgenders were on the roads. The humidity was over 90 per cent, the temperature well over forty degrees centigrade, and the dust billowed in huge clouds, forcing us to stop from time to time. The police, there to maintain discipline, were clearly insufficient in force. There was already a lot of dancing and music and beating of drums in the sweltering sun. Vendors, with portable, three-pronged food stands, were briskly selling idlis, vadas, and pakoras. Avahan's partner in Tamil Nadu, the NGO TAI, was active at the festival and we met its project director, Dr R. Lakshmi bai (who we met in Chennai, in chapter 6), after what seemed an endless last-mile journey.

At the climax of the festival, a colossal wooden statue of Aravan festooned with marigold flowers is carried by chariot, drums beating furiously, young men hanging perilously on all sides of the chariot and even from the effigy of Lord Aravan. He is wheeled slowly through the village and, at the consecrated spot, consigned to flames, symbolizing his death. The priests who had a few hours ago ceremonially married the transgenders to Aravan now cut off their talis, or wedding necklaces, and their bangles are broken to symbolize their widowhood. There is loud wailing and an overt display of heartbreak and grief. The scene is moving to witness.

We spoke with transgenders, Indian and foreign, and they included street-based sex workers, PhD students, youngsters, and grandmas. We were trying to understand the extent of safe sex, and what came in the way. A classical dance recital and an international transgender beauty contest followed. They were memorable spectacles, with great artistes, and transgenders of poise, elegance, and beauty. The beauty contestants were judged for their knowledge and accomplishments, and not just for their physical beauty.

I was looking forward to the evening's celebrations, but Dr Lakshmi bai told me that we had best head out, and fast. The revelry, she said, was wild and could turn violent, as goons wade in to disrupt and harass. 'Besides,' she said, 'anyone here at night is free game, and so would you be.' I saw the wisdom in her words and we left very soon.

~

Aravanis adopt an aggressive, mock-threatening, in-your-face posture with the public. They can make lewd suggestions and threaten to lift up their saris. They do this to scare you or to embarrass you enough to give them some money to go away. It is a means of subsistence, a deeply sad existence.

Most people are afraid of aravanis – I certainly was, to start with. Once, after I had overcome this fear, we had gone for a family picnic to Bhatkal Lake, on the outskirts of Delhi. I told my wife and sons that I wanted to stretch my legs and would be back soon. Walking briskly, I saw a lone aravani, perhaps about twenty-five, coming directly towards me. She was tall, heavily made-up, and had long, flowing hair. Wearing a bright red sari, she seemed to be hurrying somewhere with clear intent. When she saw me, she began the loud slap-clap and danced in circles around me, demanding money.

I slowly took out a hundred-rupee note, a lot more than she would have expected, and gave it to her. She folded it carefully and pushed it into her shiny plastic handbag. With a 'thank you sa'ab' she gave me a mock-blessing and was swinging away when I asked if I could walk with her. She seemed totally puzzled but said, 'Kyun nahin – why not?' I introduced myself and asked her her name. 'Juhi,' she replied. I asked her where she came from, what gharana she belonged to, and about her jamaat. She stopped walking and her eyes widened. 'How do you know all these things?' I told Juhi that I worked with her community all over India, and that her sisters had shared their traditions with me. I told her that I had even been adopted by Selvi and her jamaat in Coimbatore.

Juhi's eyes filled up. 'I'm terribly, terribly sorry, sir, I just didn't know you were a nice person.' She took out the hundred-rupee note and tried her best to give it back to me. Juhi and I went our separate ways, back into our different worlds, each with a lump in the throat.

~

There is a duality about the way people relate to the aravani. On the one hand the aravani evokes revulsion and fear. At the same time, she is seen as someone blessed by God, and in turn her blessings are valued.

In Salem, a town of about eight lakh people in western Tamil Nadu, I met the aravani Malvika, aged twenty-seven. She is sometimes known by the male name Prabhu, the name she was given at birth, which she uses on the rare occasions when she assumes her male identity. She is light-skinned, with a smooth complexion, and has beautiful, arresting eyes. This is her story:

'I was brought up in a small village, about eighty kilometres from Salem. My father had a small piece of land, which was not enough to support our family – parents, a grandmother, my elder sister, and a younger brother and sister. He worked as an agricultural labourer tilling someone else's land. He worked very hard, starting at dawn and returning totally tired out at dusk. What he made was barely enough to support the family.

'Even as a very young child I preferred to play with girls. I asked my mother to make me a ragdoll, just like the ones my friends had, and she gave it to me secretly. By the age of seven I was sure I was a girl and wondered why my body was not like my friends'. When I was thirteen I had developed feelings for boys, just as the other girls did. I had a crush on one boy in my class, and when my classmates saw that, they made fun of me. The grown-ups in the village had started whispering about me, and I received a scolding from my father. My mother always treated me with love, and I think she understood that I was really a girl, and she never hated me for it.

'Some of the men who came out of the liquor shops took me with them, and I was once seen being fondled by a neighbour. I had sex for the first time with one of the schoolteachers, when I was fourteen. The school people found out and told my father. He beat me very badly that night, and my mother and elder sister had to fight him physically to save me. This happened many times – I wanted to be loved by men and was found more and more often in love positions. Each time the news reached my father, I was beaten till I collapsed, and each time my mother and sisters and brother tried to rescue me, receiving blows themselves.

'Some incident happened, I can't remember now exactly what it was, but one day something broke inside my father. "You have brought shame on our family, Prabhu. I can't keep my head up when I walk through the village. Your sister is getting no marriage offers because of you. You are a curse on this family, and from today you are no longer my son. I want you to leave – go far away and never cast your shadow on this house again. I want you gone by the time I wake up tomorrow."

'I was sixteen, with no idea of life outside the village, and not knowing what I was to do next. My mother wept through the night. By dawn she had packed a small bag for me and she gave me five hundred rupees from her hidden savings. She said there was a train to Bombay in the afternoon that I could take from Salem, and I should leave by the next bus for that town. "Leave before your father wakes up – he may kill you," she said as she led me to the gate. She hugged me and said, "You are my darling son, you always will be, may God take care of you now." She broke down crying, and I will never forget the look on her face as I left.

'I reached Bombay the next day, and soon after met up with some aravanis, who took me to their naik, Haseena. She welcomed me into her arms and said, "From today I am your mother, and these are your sisters." In this way I started my life as a sex worker on the streets of Vile Parle in Bombay, when I was sixteen. What I earned I gave Haseena, who I called Amma, as I had called my real mother. She cooked and cleaned the house in which we lived. It had two rooms that were used with clients. There was a bathhouse with four cubicles, where one of us gave the client a hot bath after sex if he paid extra. I was terribly lonely and cried many times at night when I thought of my mother back home.

'I had developed an urge to become a real woman, by becoming Nirvana. I was told there was a doctor in Kadapa who could do the operation properly, but it was too expensive. I told Haseena, who allowed me to save some of the money I earned, and within a couple of years I had enough to go and get the operation done. I can't forget the terrible pain after I woke up, my penis and testicles gone. I remember the sheer joy I felt at the same time when I realized that I was a full woman at last. I stayed on in Kadapa and joined another jamaat there. I was more in demand now, because I was Nirvana. I was beautiful – I never did have any facial hair, and the men loved my dark eyes and smooth skin. The naik allowed me to keep almost all my earnings as more customers were coming to the house now because of me. At the same time, I got a job in a beauty salon, where I learnt make-up and hairstyling. Many clients of the beauty parlour wanted me, and I earned at least two hundred rupees a day just from tips. I made enough to buy several nice saris and wear good make-up.

'One day I got a telegram. I don't know how my sister had found me, but the message said that my mother was dying and wanted to see me. Five years after I left home, I was returning. I was dressed in my best clothes and carried my possessions in a smart suitcase. My brother received me at the station and he couldn't believe it when he saw me – but he told me that Amma had died just two days ago, and she had been cremated. It broke my heart, and my brother and I held on to each other and cried for a long time. I went to the old house – nothing was changed, only my sisters and brother were grown up, and my elder sister was married.

'When the village people heard that I had come back from Bombay, they came in a stream to see me throughout the day, no doubt they were curious. They were amazed to see me as a beautiful young woman, in a fine sari, richer, finer than theirs. Many brought small gifts and asked for my blessings. I was waiting for my father's return home in the evening with some fear, not knowing what to expect. When he saw me, sitting on the front porch with several neighbours, he came up and took me in his arms, and kissed me with great joy, calling me his precious son. I felt nothing towards this cruel man who had thrown me out of the house when I was only a child. I am more forgiving now – I realize it was not the shame so much as the fact that he would have one less mouth to feed that made him do it. The next morning, I left very early before anyone was awake, and I have never seen my family again, it's been eight years.'

Malvika joined Avahan's programme TAI in Chennai and started doing outreach work with the aravani community. She still did sex work and told me that TAI had given her a new life, and she was happy for the first time. 'What would you like to be in your next life, Malvika?' I asked on an impulse. She replied immediately, 'I know for sure I would not want to be an aravani.' She paused, then added, 'I hope I can be a bird that flies, or a nice shady tree.'

~

Chakrapani is a town with a population of 2,85,000 in Kolhapur district of Maharashtra, known as the 'Manchester of India' for its storied textile industry. I was meeting Anil, Pavan, Raju, and Sandeep, kothis from our intervention programme, to understand the environment for MSM activity in their town. Anil looked about eighteen, Pavan and Raju about twenty-five. Sandeep was the eldest in this group and looked in his late forties. The younger men were dressed in ways typical of their age – faded blue jeans, round-neck T-shirts with messages that I could not fathom, and I dare say they could not either. Sandeep looked more formal, in cotton trousers, a bush shirt, and new sandals. Interestingly he was a schoolteacher, and one of the young men had been his student, and their relationship at school had probably been something more than academic. All the three addressed him as 'sir'. They all used exaggerated feminine mannerisms, more so because a stranger was in their midst, and they wanted to flaunt their identity.

Raju told me earnestly that there was a large MSM population in Chakrapani, 'at least fifteen to twenty thousand'. He said this with some pride and looked to see if I was impressed. This was of course an exaggeration, but from what I'd seen in the two days I'd been there, MSM activity was prolific. 'How many MSMs do you think are out in the open?' I asked, meaning those that disclosed their identity. 'About two hundred and fifty at least, and each MSM would have had at least thirty to thirty-five partners,' one said, and the others nodded. This estimate also seemed too high but was more plausible. As I chatted with the foursome, I understood that MSMs had extensive social networks and most had multi-partner relationships. They would have parties – group socializing, with perhaps twenty of them crammed into a tiny room, curtains drawn, doors locked.

In the next half-hour, about ten more regular kothis joined the group. There were also a few sathla kothis, wearing saris, and a couple of aravanis. The communities blended naturally, and they all seemed like friends. There was a lot of kidding around and constant laughter. Condom usage, all admitted, was very low, even though they knew about HIV. I was told there might be a few DDs occasionally joining in their gatherings, but almost never a panthi. It was evident that there was no affection, and even some resentment, towards the panthis. Many spoke about the harassment they faced from police and local goons – they would be picked up, slapped around, money would be extorted, just because they'd been seen holding hands in a park, suspected of being an MSM. One kothi confided, 'To some extent we are protected, because the local cop is also an MSM.'

Three of the men were married and had children. 'I love my wife very much, and I am a good father,' one said. While the wives of two

men were not aware of the secret lives of their husbands, the wife of
the third knew and accepted it as part and parcel of their conjugal
relationship. It came home to me how difficult these MSMs' lives
must be, living in constant fear of being found out, unable to say out
loud who they really were.

~

In Bangalore, I meet Vasant, aged thirty-two, known in the community
by his feminine name Vasanthi or, with playful irreverence, as
Mrs Gowda – after her husband, Mr Gowda. Vasant exudes a strong
aroma of rose perfume, is thickly bearded, wears metal earrings and
an orange shirt with three buttons open, revealing a very hairy chest.
He tells me his story in halting English:

'I grew up in village. When sixteen, my brother-in-law [sister's
husband] forced me to do thigh sex. It was first sex, and it made me
happy. When I am nineteen, I came Bangalore, paid an agent, who
promised me job in police, but he ran away. I was without money. For
one year I tried find work, but no use. I had very few sex in village, but
in Bangalore I started having more and more, for money. First, it was
difficult. I wait six–seven hours without a client. Then I start learning
tricks and getting more clients. Me and some other sex workers used
an "Uncle's" house, where we brought clients we found in Mariappana
Park, which was close by.

'I call myself DD, because sometimes there would be paying kothi,
and then I could do the job other way, though I didn't enjoy. I started
going to park regularly. I fell in love with a panthi, who brought me
jewellery, but he also tortured me, so I left him after two years. Then
I met Gowda. He is controlling me every minute – even if he sees
me at bus stop he wants to know where I am going. Gowda is a very
wise man. He treats me like he is my husband. He was a lawyer at one
time, then he became businessman, and now he is moneylender. He is
married with two children. Many men don't like [when men adopt]
the female look – Gowda is like that – so I dress and act like a man.

'I love Gowda. Now only sometimes I have sex with others, just friends. I have never had sex with a woman, I don't feel like. Now I'm struggling with my problem [he refuses to say what that is]. In my next life, I don't want to be a kothi. I want to be a woman and be married to Gowda.'

When we talk to Prakash Gowda later, he is candid about his prolific sexual activity as a panthi but makes no direct allusion to his relationship with Vasanthi, his legal career, or his moneylending business, all of which might have been a fabrication or at least an exaggeration. Gowda is forty-three, stocky, dark, moustached, and radiates machismo. This is his story, told in English in a more assertive tone than Vasanthi's:

'I have been in the tile business for twenty years. Now demand for ordinary tiles is going down, so I have started doing granite tiles. I was born in Bangalore, father was agriculturist. I studied in Bangalore, up to BCom. I found out I like men when I was sixteen–seventeen. I also had sex with women. I have many kothi partners, maybe two or three every month, earlier it was many every day. There is one regular kothi partner. I fear HIV, and my desire these days is less, so I have less number of partners. I'm married, there are two children age nine and eleven, daughter and son. I want them educated, maybe my son becomes computer engineer.

'With kothi I almost always use condoms, though a few years ago, never. I have reduced anal sex, almost all thigh and oral. Kothi pay me, most times because these days there are fewer panthis. I also pay but only for new young kothi, hundred to five hundred rupees for oral. Not one person in the world knows, only community members. I even bring kothi home sometimes, but only pant–shirt types. Sometimes hijras also, we use lodges, sometimes their home. My wife suspects that I have affairs with women, not men. When my regular kothi calls on phone he uses his female name, and he can do female voice well, so my wife thinks it's woman.' At this Gowda slaps his thigh and laughs heartily. 'I control my wife. I have sex with her a couple of times per month, earlier every day,' he says musingly.

I kidded around with Gowda: 'Seems to me you are having a lot
of sex – wife, regular kothi, sometimes hijra – no wonder your tile
business is doing badly!' He again let out his hearty guffaw. But then
he said, seriously, 'Being panthi is confusing. Sometimes I'm happy,
sometimes I wonder why the hell I got into this life. What if people
come to know – lot of tension.'

~

As I grew to know and appreciate the kothi, double-deckers and
aravanis, I felt sad about their plight, living in a society that treats
them as criminals, unable to declare their identity, outcasts in every
sense of the word. Luckily, I soon earned their trust and was welcomed
everywhere I went.

MSMs in particular have a great sense of humour. They have a way
of mocking themselves and describing their most outrageous behaviour
with a deadpan expression, for shock value. As with the sex workers,
the humour is also a way to cope.

The stigma surrounding this community was so high that we sensed
that it would be more difficult to have a programme just for them. We
thought the default model should be one programme where female
and male sex workers worked together. From what we had seen so far
there was no animosity between MSMs and female sex workers, and
there were even friendships. This linking became an important part
of our model, and we will return to this in part 2.

~

It was with a little trepidation that I took Bill and Melinda Gates to
meet some people from the MSM and transgender community in
Chennai on their first visit to Avahan in 2005. I was sure they would
not have encountered people like these before, and I wasn't sure how
they would react. As we entered the small NGO centre, Bill and
Melinda stopped before a makeshift altar that had framed pictures

of Jesus, Krishna, and a picture of the Kaaba. 'God is the same,' the MSM interpreter translated. We entered a room where there were about ten MSMs and transgender people, dressed in their best, the sathla kothi in gaudy bright saris, the aravanis shaved. Bill and Melinda were enthralled.

A wonderful conversation ensued, as they asked questions with respect, listening keenly to the answers. They were asking about their life stories, and the challenges they faced today, and what change the local Avahan programme had made in their lives. It was just another conversation between human beings.

9

Back at the Ranch

Coming into the new millennium, India's HIV epidemic was being anxiously watched by the world, though the Government of India was in denial. There were many people and agencies involved with HIV prevention in India, taking on different roles, working with a single purpose – to defeat the virus. These included the World Bank; UNAIDS; the Global Fund for HIV, Malaria and Tuberculosis; international NGOs funding HIV work, for instance, the Clinton Foundation which focused on treatment; the agencies that worked on advocacy; print and television media (those were days before social media took hold); celebrities who lent their voice. I had been thrust into a lead role from the start because we had become, overnight, the largest funder in the campaign against HIV. All of us worked committedly, collaborating occasionally, reporting separately, to the grand mandarin who sat above us all – the director general of NACO.

This was mainly what I did when I was back in Delhi. In addition, in my non-field role, I engaged with the Avahan board, our technical panel, the global AIDS community, and when necessary the home offices of the international NGOs that had received grants from Avahan. And of course I stayed in constant contact with my colleagues in Seattle. My time in the field was by far the best part of my job.

The rest of it was a mixed bag of experiences – satisfying, tedious, frustrating, and sometimes hilarious.

~

Four UN system agencies played major parts – the World Bank, UNAIDS, the Global Fund for HIV, Malaria and Tuberculosis, and to a lesser extent the WHO. We had helicoptered into this august company. Unlike the hostile reception we got from the government and certain NGOs when we started out, we were received collegially by the UN system. I never got the feeling that we were viewed as interlopers.

The World Bank enjoyed a privileged position because they gave their money directly to the government.[1] Therefore, they had the most influence in shaping the content of the national AIDS control plans (NACPs), which were announced every five years. They did a good job on that most important task of keeping the focus on high-risk groups. Mariam Claeson steered the World Bank in India ably through the critical period 2006–08 when the next new phase of the national programme was being designed and launched, and where Avahan got involved in a major way.

UNAIDS is chartered with keeping the world's attention on the HIV problem, especially in Africa, and now India. Their primary role was advocacy with government. The Indian government does not take kindly to advice from foreign agencies, but UNAIDS was fortunate to have at the helm Dr Peter Piot, a globally respected virologist and expert on HIV. He also had considerable political savvy and singular personal charm. Peter was a big supporter of Avahan and spent hours with us to understand the 'business thinking' behind Avahan. His support gave our programme that much more international credibility.

The Global Fund for HIV, Malaria and Tuberculosis made country grants directly to NGOs. The fund had a tedious, brain-numbing process of grant-making that required consensus from a large number of stakeholders. I suffered through a short stint on this panel. It was a motley group of about twenty-five that included some female sex workers, an MSM, a transgender person, select NGOs, and a Christian priest. If a priest and a sex worker can agree on something, the outcome is bound to be unholy, and that could be one reason the fund's grants often turned out off the mark.

Professor Richard Feachem, the head of the fund, was, like Peter Piot, a charismatic leader. In May 2005, he made the unfortunate pronouncement from Geneva that India would see two different HIV epidemics – one affecting Hindus with a higher rate of growth and the other with a lower rate of growth for Muslims. He was alluding to recent scientific evidence that had established that HIV transmission was about six times slower without foreskin and pointing out that Hindus, who are 70 per cent of the population, are an uncircumcised, more-at-risk population. In a country with a history of Hindu–Muslim tensions, ultraconservative Hindu groups saw it as an incendiary statement. One such group, Jan Abhiyan, threatened to demonstrate outside the offices of UNAIDS. They demanded that Feachem come to India immediately and apologize in person to the Hindus of India.

Feachem from afar tried to say he meant no offence, producing the strange rationale that he was, after all, married to a Hindu. It is tough to beat a hasty retreat if you have shot yourself in one foot and have the other in your mouth, but the good professor managed. Indians don't like being lectured to by a foreigner, especially if the lecturer is right.

~

We used the term 'societal leaders' to refer to people who could use their influence to address stigma and denial. The Avahan programme worked with a varied group of these celebrities, mainly through an apex grant made to Parmeshwar Godrej's Heroes Project. Eminent writers such as Salman Rushdie, Anita Desai, and William Dalrymple contributed to our book *Aids Sutra*. India's soft-spoken cricket captain Rahul Dravid and equally mild-mannered World Chess Champion Vishwanathan Anand contributed generously of their time, spreading the message of HIV prevention. Rahul Dravid made three popular HIV public service announcements free for Avahan, in the form of videos that played on prime time. The video costs were met by us, but the airtime, which was exorbitant, was provided free by the government. In one video that is still remembered, Rahul is shown putting on every part of his cricket gear – pads, padded gloves, chest guards, and helmet. Before he steps into the field, he turns and looks straight at the camera and says, 'Whenever I step out, I always wear protection.'

We had made a grant to Parmeshwar Godrej's Heroes Project to mobilize societal leaders in the cause of HIV/AIDS. The one who made the most sustained and energetic advocacy contribution was the actor Richard Gere, his commitment stemming from his deep Buddhist faith. Richard worked very effectively in tandem with the celebrities involved, especially stars from the Indian film industry. Parmeshwar Godrej threw sparkling parties at her beautiful home on the shores of the Arabian Sea, where I felt quite out of place rubbing shoulders with the likes of Oprah Winfrey, Salman Rushdie, A.R. Rahman, Imran Khan, Salman Khan, and Shah Rukh Khan. Parmeshwar, who passed away tragically from cancer in 2016, in her own way did a lot for the cause of HIV prevention.

Before we joined hands, Richard Gere had been working with Parmeshwar for the cause of children with HIV, and on one early occasion he kept talking about their plight in a meeting with the media. I took him aside and gently suggested that though children with HIV was a tragedy, he should talk more about sex workers, which was Avahan's primary cause. His steel grey eyes narrowed and locked with mine, much as he had done so many times on the silver screen, and he said, 'You don't get it, Ashok – we talk about the kids and bring the hookers in under the radar.' The term 'hooker' is an outrage in the HIV sector, and I quickly looked around, hoping no one had heard him say the H-word. But Richard soon embraced the cause of sex workers with fervour.

Richard Gere went to many different places with the Heroes Project. In 2007 he led a rally for 15,000 wildly cheering sex workers in a football stadium in Mumbai. At every international AIDS conference

Richard spoke eloquently about the stigma faced by people with HIV in India and shamed the government for its inadequate efforts. He even convened an AIDS media summit at Prime Minister Manmohan Singh's residence in 2006. Revered by Indian actors, Richard drew stars such as Kamal Haasan who had fan clubs of millions into the fold. He also spent time in the brothels of Mumbai and other hotspots for commercial sex.

Alas, it all met with an ignominious end. In 2007, Richard was on stage at a truckers' rally in Delhi with the gorgeous Bollywood actress Shilpa Shetty. Unscripted, caught up in the moment, he suddenly swept Shilpa off her feet and bent theatrically over her, as though to deliver a kiss, while the truckers whooped and shouted. Lips never met, but news of the 'kiss' quickly reached, once again, the ultraconservative Hindu brigade, self-appointed guardians of the purity of Indian womanhood. Mass protests began, and effigies of Richard were burnt. He fled India that night, never again to return to the war against HIV in India.

His experience, and that of the other Richard before him, Feachem, exemplifies how important it is to understand cultural norms in India, or at least the goons who claim to protect that culture.

~

Avahan's technical panel, chaired by Rob Moodie of the University of Melbourne, had eighteen of the world's most respected experts in HIV. It was a two-way relationship – we received some sound technical advice from a varied group comprising scientists, doctors, and field-experienced people. David Wilson from the World Bank, Prabhat Jha from the University of Toronto, Marie Laga from the Institute of Tropical Medicine at Antwerp, business entrepreneur Arnab Gupta, Sundar Sundaraman, a respected independent expert, and Swarup Sarkar from the WHO were among those who made strong contributions. As Rob Moodie generously put it, the panel received a 'continuing education' in HIV delivery on a large scale, using what it liked to call our 'business model'. In the process, the panel members became strong advocates of Avahan and spread the good word about our work widely when they got home.

~

The extent of stigma and apathy towards sex workers on the part of elites was widespread. I remember an incident where this became evident in a public forum, when I was in the audience. It was a conference to deliberate on the challenges of HIV in India. One event was a discussion in a large panel of about fifteen people – a motley group that comprised captains of industry, celebrities, socialites, journalists, and civil society representatives.

We had brought four sex workers from one of our interventions in the South to address the panel members at this session. The sex workers were to make a presentation on how their programme worked. This was the first time any of them had ventured anywhere far from home and certainly the first time any of them had been on a plane. By the time they had checked into their rooms at the guest house, they were in a daze.

The sex workers spent all their time rehearsing their presentation. The next day, at the panel meeting, which was at Delhi's plush Taj Man Singh hotel, they explained the methods they used to estimate the sex worker population. They described how they delivered services to their community, focusing on the ones with the riskiest behaviour.

Then one of them, a male sex worker called Charu, was to tell his personal story to the panel. A lanky young man in his mid-twenties, wearing tight jeans, sharp shoes, and a bright red shirt, Charu had no written script and spoke straight from the heart for about ten minutes. Sexually abused in his childhood, rejected by family, fending for himself, barely surviving, he became a male sex worker. He had not even heard of a condom till the Avahan programme and spoke of his shock and despair when he was diagnosed as HIV positive a few years ago. His voice trembled a few times as he narrated his story.

The meeting was opened for questions, and it seemed no one quite knew how to connect with the sex worker community members. There was an awkward silence. Then one of the panel members, a prominent social worker, asked a question that made me wince.

'Now that you understand all this about HIV, about all the dangers, why do you carry on this terrible profession? Why don't you give it up? Please explain it to me.' There was a moment's silence, then Charu shot back, in a voice edged with anger, 'Madam, I do it simply because I like it.' The panel member coloured.

It was another instance of the extent of stigma that surrounded HIV and the holier-than-thou stance that people adopted so easily. I was ashamed that we had exposed our friends from the sex worker community in this way. The meeting ended and the sex workers packed up their equipment and went back home.

~

The Avahan grant money had gone to fifteen large NGOs, twelve of them well-known international agencies. Each was charged with implementing a large segment of the programme, usually a whole state. For every agency, the grant, and the programme it was meant to cover, was far bigger than anything they had done before. The grants were awarded in almost all cases by selection rather than competitive proposals, for reasons I will get to later in this narrative.

We impressed on each implementing partner that the stakes were very high. None of us had taken on something like this before, and it was important that they move fast, but always stay flexible, ready to make course corrections as new data came in and as an evolving situation demanded.

This way of working was alien to the sector. The default way of working was 'you tell us what you want done, and we'll do it perfectly'. Problems started cropping up with many of the agencies within the first six months. Our implementing partners weren't moving with speed or quality, and fresh ideas were few.

We had no option but to change the project directors of a few global NGOs to whom we had given grants. I flew to headquarters in five cities in the United States and in the United Kingdom, delivering the same message: 'If you don't fix this in three or four weeks, we will terminate this grant immediately and find someone else.' It worked – in one case the global head of the NGO, who had just taken charge the week before, flew to India immediately and stayed there for the next three weeks, putting things on course.

These were ultimately teething problems. In the end our implementing partners delivered and we worked with mutual respect and even as friends. I didn't have to speak to headquarters after that except on the rare occasion.

~

We worked extensively with national and international media, doing interviews, writing, and more often just providing background material. I learnt an important lesson in advocacy when working with media – that words are often more effective coming out of someone else's mouth.

One incident readily comes to mind. I got a call from Karan Thapar, asking if I would appear as a guest on his prime-time TV show the next day. Karan is one of India's most respected TV hosts, always well prepared, relentless in the way he grills guests on his show. I said, 'Karan, that's quite an honour, but I think I'll pass. I've seen how the people who sit in that chair opposite you get roasted!' Karan interrupted, 'No, no, you've got me wrong, Ashok. You are one of the good guys. I would never do that to you. But I know there is a lot more that the government could be doing in the fight against HIV. I want to have Yakoob Quraishi [the then director general of NACO] along with you on the show. Here's how we'll do it – you brief me on all the issues and tell me what questions to ask him. You tell me the tough questions.'

The interview began with Karan throwing some soft questions at both of us. Then he turned to Quraishi and began to roast him with his trademark question: 'Do you seriously expect us to believe . . .' As this line of enquiry proceeded, beads of sweat appeared on Quraishi's brow. During the first commercial break he had a glass full of water in a few gulps. The make-up person wiped his brow. At the end, all the tough questions had been asked of government in prime time.

In his short tenure at NACO Yakoob Quraishi did a lot of good for the HIV cause. He went on to become India's Chief Election Commissioner and he and I became friends.

~

Only when I started Avahan did I learn how painful it can be to work with some IAS officers and how frustrating it is to be at their mercy. NACO's director general was always a senior IAS officer. Everyone on stage would pay obeisance, subtly or shamelessly, to this grand mandarin.

Over two hundred thousand people take the entrance exam for the Civil Services. Of these, about one hundred are finally selected to join the elite IAS. These are exceptional people, who come from elite educational institutions as well as small rural colleges, and they begin their careers brimming with idealism. They are thrown immediately into positions of great responsibility and immense power.

The sorting into the good, the bad, and the ugly of the IAS happens within the first ten years. The good are the exceptional, idealistic officers, humble, ever willing to listen and learn. They are so rare these days that when you work with one of them, you remember him or her for life. I've had the privilege of doing that a few times in my career. The bad and the ugly are degrees of arrogant, power-hungry, disinterested, or corrupt, or all of the above. They don't take kindly to being questioned and believe they can master any subject quickly, and pass judgement on big issues within seconds. This gives the IAS officer, the more senior he is, a certain pomposity.

The main IAS officers we had to work with in my time with Avahan were the director general of NACO and the more junior officers who headed the AIDS programmes in each state. I dealt with seven directors general of NACO while I was at Avahan. I will get back to this set of relationships in part 2.

10

Scenic Route

At the massive truck stop at Namakkal in Tamil Nadu, the young NGO trainer, Poornima, introduced herself with folded hands to twenty swarthy young truckers, who had been cajoled into the HIV information session by their broker. They looked bored even before she started, lounging on a hard floor covered by a thin durrie. The trainer reached into her kitbag and took out a slightly larger-than-life wooden model of a penis. She opened a packet of condoms and expertly demonstrated the right way to put on the prophylactic, using the model as a prop. She warned the truckers never to put oil on the condom, or wear two at a time, as this might cause the condom to break. She asked for volunteers to repeat the demo and the truckers demurred, suddenly bashful. Poornima smiled and turned to the next part of the lesson, a flip chart with successive charts of a lemon and a donkey, each marked with a red X. The truckers sat up and began to take notice. They were whispering.

That was my first visit to our truckers' programme in 2004 and I understood that there was a lot I had yet to learn.

~

In a concentrated epidemic, the HIV virus moves from risk group to bridge group to general population. The risk group consists of those people most exposed to the virus, and among whom HIV prevalence is high. Female sex workers are the largest segment of this group. The virus then travels to the clients of the sex worker. These clients – the men who frequently go to sex workers – are known as the bridge group. The virus then travels across the bridge into the general population, passing from the client of the sex worker to his wife, and through her to her unborn child. It is a relentless course, and HIV prevention programmes try to stop infections from happening all along the chain. Our strategy was to focus on the core risk groups. But we also had to work on the male side. Truckers were the single largest identifiable segment of the bridge group, accounting for 10 to 16 per cent of clients of sex workers in 2001 and 2006 respectively.[1] HIV prevalence among truckers ranged from 3 to 7 per cent.[2]

The highway is the trucker's home. As prime minister, Atal Bihari Vajpayee launched a massive national highway modernization and extension programme. Running along the main north–south and east–west corridors connecting the four major cities – Delhi, Mumbai, Chennai, and Kolkata – the Golden Quadrilateral was cast in sturdy concrete and had two to four lanes. Smaller routes sprouting from these arterial roads connected with the smaller cities and towns. Vajpayee's vision gave a huge boost to the highway system and the movement of goods across the country. The length of the national highway system was about 60,000 kilometres in 2004 when we launched our highway programme.

Despite all this progress, movement along the highways was slow, with trucks rarely crossing forty kilometres an hour. Traffic, weather conditions, local strikes, and more led to huge congestions and delays of hours.

~

There were several actors in the drama of HIV transmission along the highways. The main characters were the trucker and the highway sex worker. The supporting roles were played by the owners and the brokers. Bit parts were with the police, octroi agents, poll booth operators, and myriad other money collectors.

The trucking industry was highly fragmented, and anyone who owned even five trucks was considered a serious player. Take the case of Ramavatar, a small-time trader in motor parts in Delhi's Mori Gate, who has had a good year and is wondering what to do with his windfall profit. The stock market is unpredictable, and the last time he bet on satta he had lost it all. He decides to be prudent and invest in buying a truck. He already has two trucks on the roads and his status with his peers goes up.

The truck costs about 800,000 rupees and his monthly loan instalment payment would be about Rs 12,000. Ramavatar calls his regular truck broker, Roop, and tells him with some pride that he has a new truck for him. Roop's job is to ensure the truck is utilized for at least twenty-two days every month, ideally for twenty-five. This will assure Ramavatar a nice return on his investment over and above the costs of insurance and periodic repairs and maintenance.

Brokers like Roop usually do not own any trucks. He depends on his circle of known, reliable truckers and will pick one of the experienced truckers, known as ustads, to take Ramavatar's virgin truck on its first long-distance excursion.

There are thousands of Ramavatars in the market. For the medium-sized ones, who may have thirty trucks and stay in farmhouses in outer Delhi, the trucks are also a way to convert their black money to white. When we launched our truckers' programme, there were fewer than ten large players, who own at least a few hundred trucks. The Transport Corporation of India (TCI) was by far the largest trucking company with a fleet of three thousand of their own trucks. However, on any given day, TCI could well have twenty thousand or more trucks on the highways, which they take on short-term exigent use.

At every major truck halt point along the highway system the large trucking companies would have arrangements with favourite brokers, who could be counted on to provide a truck with a reliable driver within forty-eight hours. The large manufacturing companies want reliability and enter into longer-term tie-ups with the big truckwallahs.

The brokers made extra money by overloading. When we started our truckers programme, a large truck was one that could carry a load of twelve to sixteen tons (by way of comparison, the long-distance truck running on US highways today would have a capacity of over thirty tons). Roop may decide to load the sixteen tonners up to twenty tons. He would thereby be giving a free ride for four tons of someone else's material. Ramavatar looks at this as a practice he can't control, and so the first thing he did when he bought the truck was remove factory boards and put on stronger boards so that his truck does not get damaged.

The broker is responsible for all cash costs that the trucker will need to meet along the way. He gives a few thousand rupees to the ustad to feed to the cops, octroi people, poll booth agents and myriad others who can simply stop the truck for any reason on its journey.

Ultimately, it is a series of symbiotic relationships. The truck owner and the broker need each other. So do the broker and the trucker. The trucker, the cops, and the octroi people all need each other. It's a perfect ecosystem that rarely breaks down because it runs on self-interest.

～

Sanjay Gandhi Transport Nagar (SGTN) lies in the northern part of Delhi, close to the city's borders with Haryana and Uttar Pradesh. It is Asia's biggest truck halting point, with 5000–7000 trucks idling there at any given time, and is the key transit point for trucks from across India. India's north is connected to Delhi via NH1. Two arterial highways branch out from SGTN, NH8 to the west and NH2 to the east.

SGTN is laid out in sections that correspond to the major trucking routes along the national highway system. Along these sections are the offices of the numerous brokers who specialize in those routes. Each broker has truckers attached to him who work these routes. There are also free-floater truckers who work on multiple routes and negotiate with brokers and try to get themselves the best deal.

At SGTN on a cold winter's day, I sat sipping hot milky tea with Rajesh Singh, the ustad. We sat on stools next to Rajesh's truck, watched by Sawant, his co-driver, and Chotu the helper. Truckers have a colourful vocabulary, and I discovered Rajesh's favourite word was bhenchod (sister-fucker). Rajesh first tried to avoid using this and other such terms in deference to me, but soon gave up.

'I am thirty years old,' Rajesh said – though he looked closer to forty. The wear and tear a trucker takes on his body makes it difficult to accurately guess their age, and the vanity of truckers is such that they try to hide their real age. Rajesh had just completed a long journey the previous month, driving from Delhi to Bangalore, covering the distance of 2165 kilometres in just over four days, with only a few stops for meals and rest, in a vehicle that cannot safely go over 50 kilometres an hour.

I asked Rajesh how he came to be an ustad. He told me:

'Papaji is a farmer and we come from a village near Jalandhar in Punjab. My grandfather owned eight acres of land, which got divided between his five sons. Papaji's share was very small as he was the youngest. This holding was too small for all three of us brothers, so my eldest brother went to the city and became a policeman. My middle brother farmed the land.

'As for me, Papaji thought – why not make the boy a trucker? There were about eight ustads in our village and he approached one of them, Sohan Singh, whom he knew. He said, "Puttar, take my son to be your helper. Teach him how to become a trucker like you." Ustadji said, "It is a very hard life." Papaji said, "My boy will work hard."

'Ustadji then twirled his moustache and said dramatically, "When we hit the road we don't know if we will come back alive." This was the clincher for Papaji, who took Sohan's hand, and said, "Puttar, take my son, make him a man."

'I was nineteen and I became ustadji's helper. After three years I got my licence to become a truck driver. I was happy in the beginning – I had cash in my pocket, and I saw the length and breadth of the country. I drove from Kashmir to Kanyakumari. I went to Orissa, I went to Mumbai. I felt like a real man driving this big vehicle. Those days everyone wanted their daughter to marry a trucker – but now all that is changing because of HIV. Mothers are scared.'

~

It was a challenge to design our truckers' programme. Intervention with truckers along highways had been tried before, but never anywhere near the scale of the Golden Quadrilateral. Most programmes had worked along strips of highway. The most ambitious so far had been the 'Healthy Highways' programme, started by the Department for International Development (DFID, the UK government's international aid agency) in 1996, covering two hundred sites in nineteen states. It yielded many learnings. Its one flaw, we felt, was that it was built around discrete intervention sites rather than a fluid highway network.

We decided to locate intervention points at truck halting stations along the Quadrilateral, and treat them like nodes on a moving network. We would provide HIV prevention services at all such points. The first service priority was to provide information on safe sex, to defuse the many myths that truckers believed, as Poornima did in the opening segment of this chapter. The second need was reliable treatment for STIs at programme-run clinics. Our truckers' programme partnered with brokers at each of these points; they had all lost good truckers to HIV and were willing to support any HIV prevention programme, offering their office space for information sessions.

We called our programme Kavach (meaning 'armour') and entrusted its running to the TCI Foundation (TCIF), the charitable arm of TCI. The owners of TCI, the dignified D.P. Aggarwal and his urbane son Vineet, took a keen interest in their foundation and it was always enjoyable dealing with them. Tarun Vij was Kavach's programme director and had been running his family business in steering wheels. We had recommended him to TCI as programme head, even though – like us – he had no background in HIV. We thought a person experienced in the private sector would better see this as a network solution, akin to the ones many businesses face.

After a year, we saw that we had a problem. In a tearing hurry as usual, we had embarked on a plan of setting up thirty-eight nodal points and had already contracted with local NGOs and made significant investments. Now as the data was coming in we realized that many of these points just didn't have the level of traffic we had expected. We also discovered that long-distance truckers were the ones most at risk; the short-haul truckers got home every night and didn't have much sex on the highway. At some points there was a lot of traffic, but not many long-distance truckers stopped there.

We took a tough call and decided to do a rapid restructuring of Kavach, working with Tarun, whose business acumen helped solve a tricky problem. We would cut the nodal points from thirty-eight to seventeen and close the points where there was neither the quantum nor the right mix of traffic. We saw this as a speedy course correction based on new data. We had done that already with some other grants. Many of our partners saw it as a refreshing and even exciting new way of working. Some partners, however, saw our approach as unfair, even unethical. There were strong feelings all around. In the end, the dust settled and Kavach ended up as a model for trucking programmes in HIV prevention.

~

My team spent a lot of time with truckers. We needed to understand them as people, their lifestyles, and why their condom usage was so low. Without that, we would not be able to develop a meaningful plan of action. The most learning came out of the long-distance travels we made with the truckers along the highways. The person from our team who did the most such travel was Amit Soni, a twenty-three-year-old McKinsey business analyst, who had asked to join me when I left to start Avahan.

In May 2003, Amit was at Bangalore Transport Nagar, a massive truck halting point, running a focus group discussion with a bunch of truckers. Truckers from different parts of India were present, but most were locals and they were bored. One of them suddenly said, 'If you really want to understand how we live and work, why don't you come with us?' It was then four in the afternoon, and he was set to leave no later than eight, driving north, all the way to Mumbai.

Amit called me in Delhi to ask if he could join the truckers on their journey, and I agreed immediately. By eight, he had packed a small bag and set out on the highway with Babu the leader, Gopi, his co-trucker, and Mani the helper.

~

The back of the truck was painted with ornate designs in red, black, and green, with the two messages often seen on trucks in India: HORN PLEASE and OK TATA. There was no glass on the windows, but a tarpaulin tied to the roof could be pulled down in case of rain or a dust storm. As Amit clambered in, it struck him that there were no seats. They had been removed, and instead there was just a hard, wooden bench behind the steering wheel. The bench was large enough to seat three people. There was some thin padding on the seat and more at the back, where the bench touched the body of the truck. Amit says, 'It hit me how incredibly uncomfortable it was. I was wondering how these guys could possibly sit on that bench and drive about twenty hours, eight hundred and fifty kilometres up till Mumbai. And – how would I do it. I felt very nervous.'

There was a bunk bed – just another bench – immediately above the driver. It was smaller, but adequate for one person to lie down and rest. The steering wheel was massive and, with no power steering on trucks those days, required considerable physical strength to handle, especially to reverse.

The cabin was brightly decorated. There were pictures of different gods, alongside pictures of busty women. The truckers performed a short puja, invoking God's blessings for a safe journey. It took about ninety minutes to get out on to the highway, and from then on the truck moved almost non-stop all the way to Mumbai.

~

Babu and Gopi were similar. They were both short, dark-complexioned, and pot-bellied, with thick moustaches, unshaven and generally unkempt. They looked about forty-five. One wore striped loose boxers, and the other a lungi, folded to knee length. Both had their shirts off and wore sleeveless cotton vests. They each carried a small bag with two sets of clothes.

Babu was the extrovert, while Gopi was quieter – but this also had to do with their roles as boss and subordinate. Both were from Karnataka and spoke reasonably good Hindi. Mani the helper had bright eyes, but adopted a servile demeanour, appropriate to his role. He looked about twenty.

Amit says, 'Babu spoke almost non-stop during the trip, and I learnt a lot about the ways of the truckers and the rituals of the journey from him. He largely did the Mumbai–Bangalore–Chennai route. Sometimes he would do a smaller circuit, but not stray far from his main route.

'Usually they worked in six-hour shifts with either Babu or Gopi taking turns to rest on the upper bunk. They were not very regimented about this. The helper Mani was more or less free to do what he wanted during the drive, and even got to use the upper bunk at times, when Babu and Gopi sat on the bench together, talking, arguing, joking, sometimes singing lustily. Babu told me night driving was the easiest, because there was less traffic.' Babu and Gopi said the riskiest journeys are with fresh produce, because there is a good incentive for early delivery and therefore some drivers take more risks – something they, of course, never did.

Amit says, 'Suddenly a truck is heading fast straight at our vehicle – the driver is playing chicken with us. I am terrified, thinking we are finished, but Babu swerves off into the dirt road at the last moment. Mani has to help Babu move the steering to get the truck out of the dirt, and back on the road. I realized how tough it is to handle the vehicle, and that it involved both physical strength and calm nerves.'

Liability for accidents lay with truck owners, said Babu and Gopi, who had both been involved in accidents before. 'If there is a big accident the truck driver will leave the vehicle and move on to another broker. We are more scared of the vehicle being impounded by the police, and ending in a court case. Then the brokers stop giving you business. So we try our very best to get the vehicle released quickly.'

The truck was continuously on the move and stopped only when the crew had to eat a meal or deal with paperwork. The paperwork was extensive, and the drivers didn't keep proper folders or files – the papers were loosely lying about. For every border and city limit, different papers were required. At every octroi payment point they had to wait for thirty to forty-five minutes. The standard bribe was routinely handed over, ten rupees paid openly. The payment was much higher if the papers were not in order. Babu, who handled the money, paid out loose cash like this, at least fifteen to twenty times on the drive.

Amit says, 'Babu said he was getting paid thousand rupees for the trip and Gopi five hundred rupees. I guess that Mani got something much less. I am not sure whether Babu was falsifying the numbers to win my sympathy. The extras – meals, octroi, toll fares, bribes – are all over and above the truckers' fees. They came out of a wad of cash given by the broker to Babu before the trip started, and from which he had to manage. I could see that this part followed a fixed set of rules.'

'Laughter is a big part of truckers' lives,' Amit observes. 'They have a stack of hilarious stories and are quick to see the funny side of things. One story is about a policeman who catches a trucker (whom they know) humping a sex worker in the bushes. He tells them to break it up, but the trucker keeps going. The cop ends the matter by shoving his stick up the trucker's ass. It doesn't matter if the story is exaggerated or entirely made up – Babu and Gopi laugh till they wipe their eyes, and even Mani joins in. I am also laughing out loud – they really know how to tell a story.

'The truckers have an uncanny ability to make friends. We stop at a dhaba, they don't know a single person sitting there, but soon they are all talking, having laughs, till they must hit the highway again. They are all absolute strangers, but they talk about family stuff, about their sister's marriage, and so on. They love movies and especially the superhero movie stars – they are all big fans of Rajinikanth. They listen to the radio and they love singing, and will sometimes break into song together in these chance meetings. They talk a lot, busy finding connections. They talk about women, they are very open.

'They don't like to mix with North Indian truckers. Babu tells me the North Indians have dirty sex habits, and I wonder what that means. Some Punjabi truckers told me that the "Madrasis" don't wash their hands afterwards.'

~

Truckers have a macho image of themselves, and that was obviously a big part of who they are. Babu told Amit melodramatically, 'We are always playing in the hands of death, but we don't know fear.' They thought of themselves as real men, who put their lives on the line every time they get behind the wheel. Babu told Amit, 'You are a nice guy, but for us you are always from the other side.' It was mostly bravado, and there was vulnerability just below the surface.

This macho attitude partly explained the truckers' cavalier attitude towards sex. At the dhabas and the truck stops, many had heard of

HIV, but it didn't worry them too much. Babu said, 'HIV might kill us in ten years, but this truck might kill us the next minute.' They were more scared of STIs, especially the ones that gave them boils. At a dhaba Amit overheard a trucker counselling the others, saying that if you applied some chuna on the boil it would go away. Amit was aghast that they believed such stuff.

Babu and Gopi explained the many myths linked with risky sex that truckers believe. One – which truckers all over India believe – was about garmi (heat), when they felt that their balls were on fire. The space below the driver's bench was extremely hot, and they had to keep rubber chappals on always. They believe the garmi gets into their balls, and unless it is released it will harm them. They believe that they must have sex as soon as the garmi sets in, to get rid of it. They would go to the bathroom and ejaculate if they couldn't get sex. This was one reason why truckers picked up sex workers on the highway.

They also believed that nimbu (lime or lemon) squeezed on the penis after sex will kill HIV. Amit asked them about the myth going around that you can prevent HIV by having sex with a donkey after unprotected sex. They were evasive and muttered that it didn't happen with South Indian drivers.

~

Truckers burn a lot of calories handling the steering, and this builds up a good appetite. Babu and Gopi were picky about the dhabas they stopped in and had their favourite haunts all along the route. Amit couldn't handle the food, which he found too spicy and oily, but Babu and Gopi obviously found it tasty.

The food kept changing as they travelled the distance to Mumbai. They would eat dinner around 10 p.m. – sambar–rice, with a lot of meat. Usually they ate four hearty meals and always a snack around three or four in the morning. There was either some mutton or chicken, or some other bird.

Amit recalls: 'They would routinely drink and drive at night. Babu explained that every trucker must have his quarter with dinner, or sometimes even a bottle shared between the two. Brandy was their number one drink and after that it was low-end whisky. They treated brandy as though it was medicine. The first shot was neat and the rest with water. Once I saw them placing something black under the tongue and guessed that it was a controlled substance. Babu told me it kept them awake and alert.

'They never spoke as though the considerable alcohol they had taken in could make for risky driving. They always blamed accidents on outside factors such as bicycles, scooters, or another trucker driving crazy. When they drive, I see the influence of the alcohol, but never got the sense that they were out of control.

'It's a very hard life on the road. Constant driving in dust and heat makes their skin very rough. I noticed how gnarled their hands were from handling that tough steering. Babu says, "It used to be an attractive life when I started. Now it's too rough, and young people don't want it that much."'

~

It seemed like a thankless job for the helper, Mani. In return for his apprenticeship, he had to do everything the truckers wanted him to do. His job was mainly to keep the truck clean. He would cook simple vegetables, dal, and roti, when asked to, using a small kerosene stove that was kept at the back of the truck. Mani got water for Babu and Gopi. He pressed their feet when they were tired. In tricky areas he would get off and guide the truck. He did all the odd jobs. At the dhaba, only the drivers got the cots and the helper slept on the benches in the truck. The helper was not meant to sit in the same place as a driver, so at the dhaba the truckers sat together in front and the helpers gathered somewhere at the back.

Amit says, 'Babu and Gopi called Mani by an affectionate Kannada nickname – Mundu. The truckers could deal him a slap, but for the most part 1 saw them treat Mundu with affection and let him have some fun as well. Babu said he sometimes negotiated a package price with the sex worker, which included the helper. His rest came mostly during the drive, especially if the upper bunk was available. The helper would drink sometimes but only with his own money. Occasionally there was a sexual relationship between the helper and the trucker, and they didn't hide that fact when they spoke about themselves.

'Mani said he has no clue why he is doing this job. He does it because his parents told him to. He told me he lives for the day when he gets his licence and will start driving his own truck. He says he sometimes gets a chance to practise driving in the parking lot, when Babu allows him.'

~

Amit continues his account of that journey: 'A key reason for my journey was to meet sex workers on the highway and talk to them. We keep driving for about three hours and we have not met a sex worker. I am teasing Babu, pinching his ego, which is considerable. I say, laughing, "If I don't meet a girl this is a waste of money, Babu." He suddenly stops his truck on the highway near the middle of the jungle between Davanagere and Hubli. He mutters, "The last time I stopped here there was a sex worker." He sends Mani out to find a sex worker, shouting after him not to come back unless he has found one. We are sitting there like ducks, out in the jungle looking for a sex worker, and I am thinking what the hell is going on. Mani comes back in twenty minutes with a sex worker, God knows how he found her.

'Across the trip we meet with three sex workers. One time the four of us are sitting on the main bench – Babu, Gopi, then me, and the sex worker, whose name is Gita. She looks about thirty-five, thin, and as though she's just bathed. She is wearing some cheap make-up, mainly a lot of talcum powder, to make herself look fairer. I know by now that South Indian truckers have a big preference for fair-skinned women. She has on some cheap perfume and the fragrance is overpowering within the small truck cabin. She is wearing a colourful red sari with a border. She is nicely dressed.

'I have my notepad out and I am scribbling furiously as I talk with Gita. I am trying to interview her, and these guys are trying to translate because she knows only Kannada. I was paying Gita three hundred rupees for the interview, which is a lot of money since the going rate for a sex encounter is thirty to fifty rupees. After a while Babu gets bored with the interviewing and says to Gita, "Look, the sir is paying a lot of money for this job, and you are not performing your task, why don't you perform." I say, "Don't touch me, I must write my notes." All three are coaxing her and she keeps trying to touch me in different places, giggling. Ultimately, I yell to Mani to come down and I get into the top bunk, writing notes.

'They had sex inside the truck. All three take turns, with the other two hanging around outside. I paid a hundred rupees for each one. It's a lot of money, and as we leave Gopi yells out, "Hey, there's money left – we want to see you on the way back." Gita laughs and waves as we drive away.

'I had gone in thinking there would be many sex workers at the dhabas along the way. But the dhaba owner does not want sex workers hanging around and kept shooing them away. The sex workers were usually half a kilometre on either side of the dhaba, soliciting from the highway. The driver had to get one either on his way in or out. He would negotiate the charges upfront – a single shot or a package deal. They would negotiate about things they wanted the sex worker to do. She would say what she was comfortable doing. It was a transaction. The driver would then take the sex worker about fifty kilometres down the highway, seldom more, his partner and he taking turns while the truck kept moving. The sex worker would have told them where she wanted to get out. The relationship can become semi-permanent, meeting the same sex worker each time on the highway, because the driver likes her.'

Of course there was the risk that the sex worker wouldn't get a truck in the next two to three hours going the other way to bring her back home. It is only if she has a friend on the other side of the highway that she was fine with sex in a moving truck. So sex workers preferred to have sex in stationary trucks. This was difficult because the truckers often couldn't stop because they were always chasing a delivery deadline.

The sex workers said there was no standard type of sex work on the highway. It all depended on the sex worker and her circumstances. With many women, the family knew that she was a sex worker. Gita fell into that category. The other two women on that trip were housewives, who were secret sex workers. One said, 'I have no money of my own and want to earn some just for myself.' They were all poor women – the drivers were negotiating for just thirty to fifty rupees for an act.

Amit says, 'Talking to Babu and Gopi, I got some insight into the relationship that truckers have with sex workers. Simply put, truckers really enjoy women. They treat the sex workers nicely. They don't threaten; they are not aggressive. They laugh at jokes together, get into the act slowly, rather than dive right in. The sex workers seem very accepting of the situation. Joking with the drivers, they seem to trust them. One woman described the truckers as decent people.'

Possibly everyone was on their best behaviour because Amit was an outsider – but I doubt it. We ran Kavach for almost a decade, all along the highway system. We didn't have a single bad incident and felt that by and large the encounter between the trucker and the sex worker on the highway is qualitatively different from that seen in towns, between the client and the sex worker on the street or in the brothel. It seemed almost civil in comparison.

The trucker, hurtling into pitch darkness, hundreds of kilometres ahead of him, day in, day out, is a lonely person. It may be masked by bravado, banter, or alcohol, but that loneliness is part of his life. The sex worker too is a solitary person, without real human contact. There is a strange kinship between the two. In a fleeting encounter between these two strangers, on a dark highway, there probably is an element of trust.

~

Amit ends his account: 'Coming into Mumbai, the truckers dropped me off near Powai and I felt sad leaving these guys, who I had taken a liking to. Every part of my body is paining. My feet are on fire, and my ass is totally numb. My back is aching because of all the swerving. I am covered in grime. I had made a booking at the Renaissance and the doorman doesn't let me in.'

11

Travels with the Foundation

Bill Gates made several trips to India while I led the Gates Foundation here.[1] That first trip he and Melinda made together in December 2005, exactly two years after Avahan was launched, will always be the one uppermost in my mind.

I was nervous. In Seattle a year earlier, I had been in a meeting where, appreciating the work Avahan was doing, Bill had said, 'The Avahan team is doing some amazing work in India. But we shouldn't be getting involved in delivery after this. Avahan is great, but ultimately it's an aberration.' I was told that Bill was above all a man of science, and his interest was in the development of new, cost-effective products, especially vaccines. Delivery, he felt, should be done by government and not the foundation.

In the two years that we had been operating, my team had scaled up the Avahan programme rapidly. In large measure that was because we were working with and through the community of sex workers. I wanted Bill and Melinda to appreciate that products and solutions might exist, but the know-how of delivering them on a national scale in a country as complex as India could not be taken for granted. I wanted to convey that for us scaling up was about data use, advocacy, and an

155

empowered community at the centre of it all. The word 'aberration' that Bill had used about Avahan rang in my ears, and I was all keyed up about getting this message across, in the very limited time we would get with Bill and Melinda.

Bill's three days in India were to be split between Microsoft and the foundation, and we could get only one Avahan day in the field with him and Melinda. We decided to take them to Chennai, because there they could see both treatment and prevention aspects at work and meet members of most high-risk groups.

In the evening the foundation held an informal high tea, for Bill and Melinda to meet with about twenty-five invitees from politics, government, sport, the arts, and philanthropy. It was an odd event, with many guests spouting inanities with great gravity. One of them told Bill that HIV was spreading because of all the extramarital sex they showed on television. Someone told me that foreign tourists having sex with camel-boys was the root cause.

The small tea party was followed by a reception for over three hundred guests, all people who were associated with Avahan in some capacity. Bill and Melinda mingled with the crowd. At one point, an aravani from Chennai, dressed in a glorious Kanjeeveram silk sari, came up and touched Bill's feet, taking him by surprise. She took his hand and said 'TG', with a charming smile, and Bill turned to me with a puzzled look. When I explained that the aravani was introducing herself as transgender, Bill and she both burst out laughing, a picture that was beautifully captured by a photographer.

~

The third day of Bill and Melinda's visit was reserved for Avahan. It was deep winter in northern India, and the infamous Delhi fog had set in. Visibility was poor, and the plane took off almost two hours late. My colleague Jacquelline Fuller, who led advocacy and communications for Avahan, was with me.

After landing in Chennai, our plan was to go straight into a meeting with the Avahan team, and then visit Tambaram Hospital, Asia's largest HIV treatment facility. Jacquelline whispered to me that because of the flight delay one of the events would have to be dropped, and it was my call which one that should be. My team was very excited about this meeting and they had prepared hard for it. I wanted Bill and Melinda to see how good they were. But I made the hard call to drop the team meeting.

I had never been inside a private plane and had only seen images of the flashy personal aircraft that many of India's corporate elite used. India's beer baron used a refurbished Airbus 319 as his palace in the sky. The aircraft that Bill and Melinda used was much smaller than I expected, but comfortably furnished. There was a kitchen galley as we entered, and a small sitting room with a few soft leather armchairs. Bill and I sat facing each other, and just across were Jacquelline and Melinda. The last section of the aircraft could be converted into a small bedroom.

There were a couple of mishaps during the flight that I still recall with embarrassment. I was keen to show Bill and Melinda some photos from the field, to give them an idea of the settings in which we worked. The images had been captured by one of India's best photographers, Prashant Panjiar, and I had assembled them in sections on my digital media player. Jacquelline and Melinda pulled their chairs over, and I pulled out the device.

I felt a little kick on my shin from Jacquelline, who was looking at me sharply. Something was wrong, but I wasn't sure what. Melinda gently took the device from me and went slowly through the pictures. Bill glanced at them, and then looked out of the window. That evening I asked Jacquelline why she had kicked me. 'You don't pull out an iPod and place it before Bill and Melinda, Ashok. Gosh, don't you know such things?'

I honestly didn't know such things, and I was mortified. 'Don't worry about it, they didn't seem to mind,' she said, when she saw my expression. 'Umm – can we keep this little event between us, Jacquelline?' I said. 'Of course, boss,' she replied, 'my lips are sealed.' Jacquelline of course told the team with great glee, and the story is recounted to this day of how Ashok shoved an Apple product into the face of the founder of Microsoft.

Then the second mishap happened. I had loaded my foundation laptop with a set of slides that had a lot of data and analyses that showed the complexity of the epidemic, and our game plan. With the constrained space, I had to keep the laptop facing away from me. That was not a problem, because I could rattle off the content in my sleep. Bill was engrossed in the presentation, when to my horror, the screen froze, and no matter what Jacquelline or I did, it stayed frozen. Bill reached over, took the laptop, and spent a couple of minutes tapping out instructions on the keys. After a minute the screen came alive again. 'It was a hardware problem,' Bill said pointedly. 'Let me show you what to do if this ever happens again.' He took me through a set of commands that opened some pop-up windows that enabled you to diagnose where the problem was. I hadn't the slightest clue what Bill was saying to me as by now, after the stress of the whole experience, it was my brain that had frozen. I just kept nodding my head. After all, my computer was being fixed by the most knowledgeable IT help in the world.

My brain soon thawed, and we went back to the slides. I was trying to convey some key messages through this presentation: the complexity of the problem essentially because of the absence of data, the 'invisible consumer', the overall stigma. I discussed the central role of community and the need for eventual transition. To my dismay, I saw that Bill had come in with a simplistic view, that essentially the problem was about getting the condoms out. But he showed interest in the slides and dived deep into the more detailed ones. The discussion moved smoothly and quickly, and by the end of an hour he had absorbed the many and complex dimensions of HIV in India.

What struck me about Bill in this first meeting, and then ever since, was that he always has the attitude of a student. In meetings, he inevitably has his yellow pad in hand and scribbles notes, asking questions all the time. It was instructive how quickly he would discard or adjust an assumption he had made, as soon as he saw data that showed otherwise. Bill later said this review of the data during the flight was one of the highlights of the trip for him. What if that screen had stayed frozen? I shudder to think of it!

~

Excitement and emotion were in abundance when we landed in Chennai. There was an enormous crowd at the airport, made up mainly of media and the curious public. The foundation's security people provided a human cover for Bill and Melinda and moved them quickly to the waiting Mercedes van. I managed to stay just behind the security ring and jump into their van. People pressed against the windows, smiling and banging at the windows, their way of welcoming Bill and Melinda to their city. I noticed that their responses were genuine and they were not in the least bit annoyed by the boisterous reception.

It was a short drive to Tambaram Hospital, on the outskirts of Chennai. On the way, Bill was fascinated by the cityscape. 'I've never seen a city quite like this,' he said. 'Where do all the cows come from?' I explained that the cows were released once they stopped producing milk, since they were considered sacred and could not be slaughtered. I told him how in Delhi the administration was working on a scheme through which any person who brought in a stray cow would be paid Rs 2000. The cow would then be made to swallow a device whereby it could be tracked anywhere. Why it would be useful to track an abandoned cow was not obvious. Melinda found the proposed plan hilarious.

The point was also not lost that while all this consideration was being given to cows, thousands of people were dying of HIV and no one seemed to care. Bill and Melinda were deeply moved when we toured Tambaram, as they went from bed to bed. They would occasionally stop to talk to a dying man, hold his hand, find out more about him as a person.

~

Later that day we left for the office of ARM, an NGO working mainly with MSMs and the aravani population. The office was a house in a lower-middle-class residential area, and to my relief the narrow approach road was free of crowds as the NGO had managed to keep the visit completely secret.

We were greeted with the tilak, dhup, and marigold flowers that are traditionally offered to honoured guests. We came into a room where there were a dozen people – seven female sex workers, three kothi MSMs and two aravanis. A few media people travelling with Bill and Melinda were allowed in along with the NGO staff, adding another dozen people to that crowded room.

Bill and Melinda had the ability to completely shut out everything extraneous and focus on the community of sex workers. They sat cross-legged on the floor, facing the community members who were sitting in a small circle. Melinda asked some of them if they would relate their stories. All the tales were sad ones – of rejection, utter poverty, and then somewhere a spark of hope. They were brutally honest and raw. One aravani narrated how she had been thrown out of her home by her father (the story of Malvika/Prabhu in chapter 8) and her story clearly disturbed Bill.

There is a story from another meeting that day with female sex workers that stands out in my memory. One of the women related how she had hidden the fact that she was a sex worker from her daughter, who was then in high school. When the mother was found out and exposed, the girl was relentlessly teased, harassed, and ostracized by her classmates. She must have fallen into deep depression. One day her mother came home to find her child hanging from the ceiling fan, and a note left behind saying she could not take it any more.

I noticed that Bill, next to me, had his head down and was crying quietly.

~

The day in the field in Chennai with Bill and Melinda was coming to an end. I got a few minutes with Bill before they left. 'I realize what you are doing here has very little to do with HIV,' he said. 'What you all are doing here is building a type of social capital that is amazing, by transforming the lives of these people who are in such bad circumstances. As far as I'm concerned even if you don't avert a single infection you would have been hugely successful.' Just hours after he had gone into the field, Bill had appreciated that Avahan was essentially about communities. It put wind in our sails.

Over the years I have been with Bill in many discussions in the field. I observed that the reason he got so much out of these conversations was that he treated the very poor and desperate as equals – as fellow human beings. On their part, the members of the sex worker community were not impressed by the fact that they were in the presence of Bill Gates. In their circumstances, he was just another human being, with whom they were having a conversation as equals.

Bill made regular trips to Avahan after that, and so did his family. I like to think Avahan played some role in getting Bill to adjust his stance from just product, to product and delivery. In 2007 the whole Gates family except Melinda came on another trip – Bill Senior, his wife Mimi, Bill, and his sister Libby. We were all together in a brothel in Budhwar Peth, Pune's red-light district, sitting in a madam's room talking with a group of sex workers. Bill Senior, whose son shares his wry sense of humour, said with a chuckle, 'In other families, a father takes his kids out on a normal vacation. And look where I've brought my kids!' When his words were translated, the sex workers broke into peals of laughter.

Part II
Learning to Fly

Blackbird singing in the dead of night –
Take these broken wings and learn to fly,
All your life, you were only waiting
for this moment to arrive.

– John Lennon and Paul McCartney

Prologue

With Avahan, from my very first day in the field out in Vizag, I was transported into an India that I never knew existed. My team and I understood that we needed to learn all about the communities that were most at risk of getting infected by the HIV virus, if we were to serve them. That is why we leapt into the field and remained closely engaged with the people there throughout Avahan. That is what gave us some insight – and credibility.

In part 1 I described my travels across India to meet these communities. They were the female sex workers, MSMs, transgender people, injecting drug users, and truckers. Understanding and empathizing with the life circumstances of these people, and therefore why they took the risks they did, was the only way to develop and deliver solutions on a large scale to stop the spread of HIV. Soon I realized that we didn't have answers. The solutions had to come from, and be implemented by, the people most vulnerable to HIV because only they truly understood the problems. Our job was to enable and support. It would have to be a real partnership.

The biggest such population group comprised the female sex workers, and in part 1 I described the complex challenges of working with these women. The first was that female sex workers were, for the most part, dispersed and mobile. We saw this in Kakhandi village

167

(chapter 5) in North Karnataka and later in the Budhwar Peth brothel in Pune. The second was that these women were in effect invisible, because they did not present themselves in any obvious way as sex workers. We witnessed that in the scene in Hyderabad in the same chapter, when the sex workers looked like a group of housewives arrived for a tea party. It was also evident soon after at the office of the NGO CHES in Chennai, when we pored over a map of a large, respectable locality of the city, and saw a rash of red dots, depicting the locations of the sex workers 'hidden' in the street.

But there was an even bigger problem. This was the fact that even if sex workers were found, they were very often not interested in HIV prevention. They had more immediate calamities to deal with, the biggest of all being the violence they faced as part of their everyday lives. It was the kind of brutality described in chapter 3, when Kamla in Medak was gang-raped while her babies lay in the dust; by Theni in Dharmapuri, who was slapped hard by a client and told to spread her legs when she tried to get him to use a condom; and by Parvati in chapter 6, who was tortured and burnt with acid, by goons paid to do that by her former husband.

Underlying all this was the wretched human condition of these women – often dirt poor, lacking physical or emotional support, with no money, and no ability to stand up and ask for the entitlements of shelter and safety due to every citizen.

The reader who has come so far could well ask: how then did we reach sex workers who were dispersed, mobile, invisible, and indifferent? How could we possibly work with people who were so marginalized and stigmatized?

Part 2 tries to show how this happened in one location, primarily with female sex workers. The site I have chosen is Mysore. It describes how Ashodaya, the Avahan programme in that city, blossomed out from arid conditions. I do this by trying to take the reader out in the street and into the room as the sex workers made and implemented plans. This story is also told through the personal narratives of two sex workers involved with Ashodaya from its earliest days, Kavita and Shahid, whose lives bear testimony to their incredible resilience and courage and, above all, to their ability to find love in the face of impossible odds.

Why focus on the female sex worker and not on any of the other community groups? The simplest answer is that they were by far the largest highly at-risk group we worked with. I could just as well have told of the adventures of working with MSMs, transgender people, drug users, and truckers, but this would have become far too long a narrative – perhaps another time! But the principles we applied with the women held true everywhere.

Why choose Ashodaya for this telling, when it is just one of the many outstanding programme sites that were embedded in the vast landscape of Avahan? Heroic battles were being fought in many other places at the same time. The main reason I chose Ashodaya is that it still exists, and because it has become a model. Every other Avahan programme district was handed over to the government in the period 2009 to 2012 as part of our exit plan. Ashodaya has become a global learning site that today receives government officials, implementers, sex workers, and students from across the world. Because it is still there, some who read this book may feel inclined to visit, contribute, and become not only part of Ashodaya but of the larger cause of human rights. Ashodaya is a microcosm of the Avahan programme. The story of that microcosm as depicted here follows a rough chronology – from desperate beginnings to better times.

Avahan expanded rapidly to become the largest-ever HIV prevention programme in the world. We made a strong contribution to stopping the growth of HIV and bringing it to a point where levels of HIV infection in India are among the lowest in the world today. By going deeper into one town and one site, the reader may get at least a partial answer to that entirely appropriate question: yes, but how exactly did it all happen?

12

The Other Mysore

The first time I barely noticed, but ten minutes later, I felt it again. Someone had scratched my palm three times with a finger, so fast that I noticed only after it had happened. 'Don't mind, sir, he is only offering you,' said Shahid, the male sex worker, apologetically. Now I understood it was only a friendly invitation to sex, from a total stranger. I looked around and couldn't make out from where the touch had come. Sensibly, I put my hands in my pockets.

It was December 2003, and I was exploring the streets of the graceful, old-world city of Mysore by night, guided by a few sex workers. It was my first encounter with the other Mysore.

~

Mysore is the third biggest city in Karnataka and had a population, in 2003, of almost 800,000. Located in the foothills of the Western Ghats, the city has a salubrious climate, with a cool breeze that begins to blow precisely at seven every evening. Mysore was the capital of the massive kingdom of Mysore for more than five hundred years, right up till 1956. Successive Mysore maharajas of the Wadiyar dynasty ruled in almost unbroken succession throughout this period. The maharajas were known for their fabulous wealth and for their patronage of education and art. The fabled Mysore Palace is the city's prime tourist destination, with hundreds of visitors every day. The open area just outside the palace gates, I discovered, was one of the city's major hotspots, something that only a few purposeful visitors knew.

The people of Mysore are soft-spoken, a typical southern Karnataka trait. With its soothing air, heritage of arts and education, and imposing architecture, the city exudes a genteel aura, like an old dowager.

~

In the first year of Avahan, our team fanned out to visit various districts and towns within our six programme states. The Government of India had started HIV prevention programmes in several districts in each high-prevalence state, but had not made contact with most of the people needing services. For example, in Andhra Pradesh, NACO-funded programmes reached only 33 per cent of people most at risk of contracting the virus, according to the government's own estimates; in Maharashtra that figure was 21 per cent, in Tamil Nadu 40 per cent, and in Karnataka 39 per cent.[1] This meant two out of three people most at risk were left vulnerable, without any kind of HIV prevention services.

Avahan was determined to close the gap and we set to work with a great sense of urgency. In Karnataka, the University of Manitoba had a project called ICHAP (India-Canada HIV AIDS Project) headed by Dr Jamie Blanchard. Jamie was that rare combination of rigorous academic and grass-roots practitioner. ICHAP was running HIV prevention programmes in two districts in North Karnataka. They were doing a good job and were familiar with the state, and to us they were an obvious choice as partner. Not wasting any time, we had handed the entire Karnataka grant to ICHAP, without calling for proposals. Jamie and his colleagues looked stunned when we told them the news.[2]

~

Shahid moved briskly across the street to get to a less crowded section and I asked him to stop at a chemist's shop. I looked for a packet of condoms, but the youngster behind the counter didn't understand my request. His boss stepped up and said they didn't stock condoms. A little further, we stopped at a paanwallah's kiosk, and he sympathetically suggested we try a chemist two blocks away. They didn't keep condoms either but suggested that we try at the government hospital. In other parts of India NGOs involved in HIV prevention were virtually dumping condoms across busy towns. I had assumed chemists in the centre of Mysore would stock them. What did the virtual absence of condoms suggest about the growth of HIV in the city?

We navigated crowded streets and arrived at the city's big interstate bus stand. Here, all through the day and into the night, buses left and entered the city from across the state, and from neighbouring Kerala and Tamil Nadu. The depot was large enough to accommodate about thirty buses at a time. Now, at 10 p.m., it was humming with activity. Porters hauled luggage to be tied on to the roof of the vehicles. The loud cries of bus conductors in khaki, calling out their destinations, rang in the air. A wandering vendor of savouries wrapped in newspaper called out, 'Time pass! Time pass!' Another moved around briskly with steaming coffee in short glasses, ascending the decibel scale with 'Kap, kap, kap, kaaapi!'

I had been told the bus stand was a vibrant pick-up place for both male and female commercial sex workers, but I couldn't spot anything. Neelamma, the female sex worker in our small group, had disappeared and soon came back with three women, who wore simple saris and carried modest handbags. Nothing in the way they dressed or comported themselves suggested that they were sex workers. In fact they looked like typical middle-class housewives. They told me that their regular clients always knew where to find them in the bus depot. Otherwise, they used signals to convey who they were. Men who frequented sex workers always knew these signals. After a short negotiation with the client, they went to one of the many lodges in the area where they had a work arrangement, and rented a room for either a short time or an all-night encounter.

We said goodbye to the women and made for a municipal park just behind the bus stand, with large, shady trees and dense foliage. Some male sex workers had gathered in the darkness to meet us, sitting on the raised cement platform around a large tree. A lot of banter, and some friendly pushing and shoving, was going on. Unlike the women, they were a boisterous, colourful lot. Several varieties of male sex workers, organized by Shahid, had come to meet me. Some, the 'pant–shirt kothis', looked like regular men and did not stand out. Of the others, there was a sathla kothi and an aravani – a young man with long, painted nails and long hair tied high on his head. Their ages ranged from the early twenties to the forties. Santhu, the eldest of the group who looked like he was past seventy, kept a dignified distance from the youngsters. 'He has no teeth,' one of them said, 'and that's why we have no clients.' There was raucous laughter.

From the bus stand, we went to three more hotspots – the railway station, the area around Mysore Palace, and the circle at one end of Sayyaji Rao Road.

~

Those are the scenes I remember from that first visit I made to the other Mysore, soon after Avahan had started.[3] It was a place where sex work was vibrant, no one had heard of a condom, and HIV prevalence was high. As I flew back to Delhi the next day, I wondered how we could ever create a successful HIV prevention programme in this city, never imagining that a young woman doctor would trigger a miracle here in Mysore in a matter of weeks, through the programme that came to be named Ashodaya.

~

Having received our grant in October 2003, ICHAP immediately started sending fact-finding teams all over Karnataka to determine which districts and towns they should focus on. They tried to understand what drove the epidemic in each district by talking to sex workers and visiting the hotspots where sex was being bought and sold briskly. They were looking out for the people they called 'gatekeepers' – those who could enable, or prevent, access to the community of sex workers in that town. These included lodge owners, police, and NGOs already working with the community.

One of these teams was led by Dr Sushena Reza-Paul, a diminutive doctor who had joined ICHAP a year earlier. That team also had Kaveri Gurav, a young anthropologist from the ICHAP project in North Karnataka; Senthil Murugan, who had been running a small NGO in Chennai and had worked with DFID; and Dr Sundaraman ('Sundar'), who had been involved with HIV prevention programmes in India from their earliest days. The four were at the end of an exhausting three-week expedition that had led them more than a thousand kilometres down the length of the state – from Dharwad and Bijapur in the north, through Bagalkot and Shimoga, and finally to Bangalore and Mysore in the south.

In Mysore, they first had to get to know the sex workers. Without any useful contacts, they approached the autorickshaw drivers, because in small towns they are often the most knowledgeable people about where sex work is happening. The drivers, like unusual tourist guides, told them about the different hotspots in town. They all pointed the team to Sayyaji Rao ('SR') Road.

SR Road and its environs appeared as if it had been carefully designed for sex work. At one end of the road was the Ayurvedic Hospital Circle, which was called 'SR Circle' by the sex workers. The circle was always busy with traffic and there was a park with thick foliage on almost all sides. Here, young men and transgender people, in tight T-shirts or bright saris, waited to be picked up by one of the cars. As dusk set in, women who looked like ordinary middle-class housewives appeared one by one, along the perimeter of the circle. The women did not look at the men who passed by – they had to be approached, such was the protocol. Couples would walk casually, one some distance behind the other, to one of the nearby lodges, or disappear for a few minutes into the foliage.

The real action, though, was on SR Road itself, which runs for about seven hundred metres from SR Circle to the City Bus Stand. It was a major commercial area, lined with stores and cafes on both sides. The busy period began from 6 p.m. and at its peak there would be as many as eighty to a hundred sex workers, mainly female, along the road. They had their own beats, agreed upon through a loose, tacit arrangement. Sometimes turfs were intruded upon, and clients stolen, which could lead to loud, even violent, arguments, on the street. Behind SR Road was a labyrinth of smaller roads, narrowing into lanes. Dotting this maze were well-known lodges with names like Anitha, Somnivas, Vayurathya, and Maurya. Many lodges rented out rooms by the hour for commercial sex activity. Sex workers brought their clients to these lodges after a pick-up on SR Road.

One of the narrowest lanes, known in Kannada as 'onduvare anni gali'[4] (roughly translatable as 'ten paisa lane', connoting its tiny size), was difficult to find unless you were experienced, and therefore it was a favoured destination. The network of lanes was also useful because when the police raided SR Road, the sex workers could scatter into the maze of lanes. Sushena and her team were experienced enough to spot the sex workers. But the women just moved away, unwilling to speak when Kaveri and Sushena approached them.

The visiting team went to the railway station because they had been told that this was also a major hotspot. A friendly autorickshaw driver introduced them to a sex worker there, who was willing to speak for a couple of minutes. She said that sex activity happened inside stationary trains, as well as on the Mysore to Bangalore night train. They would also pick up clients on the platform and take them into the bushes that were plentiful around the station for oral sex or a quick encounter.

~

Unable to make much progress, the next morning the team approached the only two NGOs in Mysore working with sex workers – Surya Kiran and Sarvodaya. Surya Kiran was distributing condoms to the local MSM population. Their contacts with the communities of men or women most at risk were limited. But they made a useful connection there, an MSM named Charu (whom we met at the board meeting in chapter 9), who was friendly and curious, and was to join the group later. Sarvodaya was a church-based organization that looked at sex work as a sin and tried to put women into rehabilitation. The visiting team's approach was to look at sex work as a profession and focus on reducing risk in that work. They were getting frustrated – it was day two, and they had made little headway.

They told Sarvodaya that their work was wonderful, and asked if they could be introduced to a few women whose lives they had changed. After some initial hesitation, Sarvodaya suggested that they meet Suranjana. She was in her late thirties, confident and assertive, and, like many sex workers in Mysore, looked like the housewife next door. Suranjana told Sushena that she ran a chow mein centre and that her boyfriend looked after the shop most of the time.

'Then can we go and try some of your chow mein?' Sushena asked. 'Maybe we can have some coffee together, and you can call your friends also.' Suranjana was taken aback, pleased that they were all going to visit her eatery. On the way, she confided that Sarvodaya gave her an allowance, supposedly to run the chow mein centre and to keep her out of sex work, but it was a pittance and she made more money from just a few clients during a festival.

Suranjana's restaurant was a small hut. Her scrawny boyfriend, Raju, sat behind a counter, intently watching a cricket match on

TV. He could have been cast in stone except for a slow, rhythmic scratching of his crotch, and an occasional muttered expletive when a ball was fumbled. A lone customer sat eating chow mein with his fingers in one corner.

Suranjana called five of her friends, and soon word got around. Within an hour five more curious women had arrived. Raju got up from his stool and threw some noodles into a large wok, never taking his eyes off the screen. The women didn't say that they were sex workers, but it was understood. Meeting like this, eating together, sharing coffee, just chatting with people who had come from outside, people who weren't judging them, was a big new experience for the women.

Suranjana trusted Sushena after that first meeting. Late that afternoon she took Sushena and Kaveri to the field to meet more sex workers. Her introduction made a difference, and some of the women spoke freely. After a while, they readily accepted Senthil and Sundar when they came by. Sex workers tend to be good judges of people, and they quickly read the body language and attitude of these visitors, even though only one of them – Kaveri – spoke the local language, Kannada. While sex work in Mysore and Bangalore looked similar, there was one difference – the women in Bangalore seemed hard in comparison. In Mysore there seemed to be a gentler southern Karnataka culture, of openness and acceptance.

~

The team was in the field the rest of the day, moving to different hotspots with Suranjana. By late evening they had reached the City Bus Stand and there they met a male sex worker called Shahid for the first time (the same Shahid I introduced at the beginning of this chapter, whom we will meet again later). He had been diagnosed as HIV positive just two days earlier, and his wife was soon to have their fourth child. He was worried sick, crying, at a complete loss. Within minutes he had shared all his problems with the visitors. I asked Sushena whether Shahid trusted her because she was a doctor. She says, 'Not at all. It was more because of human contact than anything else. He was overpowered by emotion and we were hugging him, bringing him something to eat, and so on. Walking towards the Mysore Palace gates after that, he told me he didn't want Charu – his good friend, who had joined the group – to know.' Shahid had been observing the visitors moving around, watching how they behaved. He had been at the SR Circle the previous evening. For the next two days Shahid and Charu took Sushena's team through the main roads and the streets where sex work was happening. The team talked to several lodge owners. At the government's HIV testing centre, they were taken aback when they found that over fifty people tested positive every month. There was no treatment available.

They spent three days like this, just walking the streets from morning to night, talking to sex workers, meeting the gatekeepers, trying to understand what was driving the spread of HIV in Mysore.

Sushena estimates that in December 2003 there were only about ten HIV prevention programmes working with sex workers in all of Karnataka. There was no well-documented and widely accepted model in Karnataka – probably nowhere in India – on how to reduce the vulnerability of street-based sex worker communities to HIV. The best-known model of intervention was Sonagachi, which was in a brothel-based setting. They were aware that they were in territory unfamiliar to almost anyone.

~

Having travelled across Karnataka, Sushena's team was most excited about working in Mysore, even though it would be a difficult place to set up a programme with so much risky sex and a virtual absence of condoms and reliable STI treatment. It is difficult to pinpoint why they were most eager about Mysore, but it probably had something to do with the resilience already evident in some of the sex workers they had been meeting.

In December 2003 they came back to Bangalore and made a presentation of their findings to Jamie Blanchard and the ICHAP team. They recommended that ICHAP in Mysore implement Avahan's grant directly rather than through any NGO. They proposed that it should be built into a demonstration site. The team promised that within twelve weeks they would have services to sex workers being delivered in Mysore through a fully operational programme. The ICHAP team and the state government people were a little sceptical, but gave the go-ahead. I had been following developments myself after my visit to Mysore soon after Sushena's team had been there, and backed the idea. It certainly had to be tried.

~

The team came back to Mysore from Bangalore on Christmas Eve, 2003. They had set themselves an impossible deadline of twelve weeks to create a vibrant programme from nothing. There was no plan then to create something big and lasting. There was only the feeling that they had to get as many sex workers as possible together and start providing services to keep sex workers safe from HIV. They instinctively realized that the only way to figure out how to proceed was by asking the sex workers themselves.

They needed some local people on the team and recruited a post-graduate in psychology and a fresh graduate. They reconnected with Shahid and Charu and started making extensive field visits. This time they included the police, local leaders, and landlords, finding out who did what, and who they could work with. To gain a toehold they said they had come to start a project for female sex workers' health. They mentioned Avahan and the Gates Foundation. That opened doors with the police and some of the gatekeepers but held little meaning for the sex workers.

They reconnected with Suranjana, who was their main contact with the female sex worker community. In the initial meeting with female sex workers it was about having coffee, checking each other out. The visitors would always introduce themselves in a way that the sex workers could relate to. Sushena told me, 'It was a woman-to-woman conversation, and that always works well. I told them about my family, about my broken marriage. I spoke of the mental and physical abuse I had endured in my life. I often brought my two girls, who were then in sixth and fourth grades. They knew the women by their names and called them Aunty Rani, Aunty Aisha, and so on. Our attitude was, if you want to, stay on – if not, that's also okay. We told them we had not come with any solutions and told them about our limitations.'

Sex workers are not used to being treated with respect. Almost everyone they dealt with – husband, boyfriend, police, landlords, and the public – views them with contempt, exploits and even violates them. The newness of being treated with respect opened a floodgate of emotions. Sushena recalls that one said, 'No one has shared a coffee with me before from the same cup. Even my family wouldn't do that – how do you do that?'

The team asked the sex workers what they needed most. They said, 'If you want to work with us do something about violence from police and rowdies which is unbearable.' The implication was that only then would they know that the visitors were genuine. Then they said, 'Give us a space from one to four in the afternoon, we have no clients then and we need a safe space.' Finally, they said, 'We want our own clinic.' STIs are an occupational hazard, whenever condom usage is low, and a reliable, discreet clinic was the most pressing requirement.

The visitors hadn't told the sex workers what they had come prepared to give them. Instead, they had asked what conditions the community would set to give them the privilege of serving them. It was a reversal of roles and it made all the difference.

No one said 'keep us safe from HIV'. Preventing HIV was just not on the sex workers' list of priorities. It was the same message I had heard from Rajamma on my first field trip. It was the same message I had been hearing from sex workers all over India in those early days, and it had caused me so much despair.

The team didn't talk about HIV at all. It was clear that violence was the main problem, and the clinic and the safe space the immediate needs. In response to the request for protection from violence, the team said, 'We are here to help. But you know, and we know, the problems with police and rowdies won't go overnight. We promise you we will try our best, but we need your support.' They were always careful not to overcommit.

~

The team had given out their phone numbers and the sex workers kept calling Kaveri and Sushena, even in the middle of the night. There were a few incidents that built trust and acceptance with the community of sex workers in Mysore.

For instance, Sushena was woken by a call from a sex worker at 1.30 a.m. The caller was crying, saying that one of them had been picked up by a certain notorious police inspector who was widely feared. They all knew that if any woman fell into his clutches, she would get a severe beating, and possibly much worse. Sushena and Kaveri rushed to the police station and introduced themselves as Avahan workers. Sushena recounts the lively conversation that followed: 'The police said these are bad women. I said but what have they done? He said they were in a room with a client. I said under which penal code have you arrested them? He said a mobile was stolen. I said what proof do you have?' The police inspector was the one being cross-questioned, and it must have been a first for him. A big, burly man, he found it difficult to keep up with the tiny woman in front of him. She was insistent, though not confrontational. It was getting awkward in front of his staff. The inspector let the woman go.

Other incidents did not have such happy endings. A woman called Mala had been brought to the police station. She was seven months pregnant and her 'husband' had kicked her in the stomach. She was writhing in pain and bleeding, and Sushena could see that she would abort soon. They rushed her to a hospital, where she aborted safely.

Another incident involved a young woman called Manjula, also called 'Sundari' because of her beauty, who had been raped and robbed by the police in Chamundi Hills on the outskirts of Mysore. She managed to give Kaveri a call and they rushed to her rescue but reached too late. In these cases, even though the team could not prevent the worst from happening, the fact that they had responded immediately made the community trust and believe in them. The team understood a cardinal principle – you cannot work with communities unless you have established trust, and you can't rush that process.

One incident was particularly important. Sushena was walking on SR Road when she heard a loud commotion, women running helter-skelter. Neelamma, a sex worker who was working with them, was screaming at Sushena – *run, run*! Sushena managed to grab Neelamma's hand and held her tightly. Two policemen came running straight towards them, wielding sturdy lathis. Sushena stood still, holding Neelamma, who was shivering in fear, expecting a lathi blow at any moment. Sushena confronted the police, told them she was a doctor, and about their programme to stop HIV, explaining that Neelamma was a programme worker. The police backed down and even apologized.

Sushena says, 'There is an interesting thing – it was not all one way. I found out that if sex workers know you are not there to harm them, they will also protect you from any harm. This was important because the work was risky for us too. We were after all women, easy prey for local ruffians. We had some bad experiences with men, but the sex workers always moved in, both male and female, and protected us.'

~

The team used to meet at a place called Modern Café on SR Road, which still exists. Its owner was sympathetic to sex workers, though it was understood that the cafe would never be used as a pick-up spot. He even allowed a space at the back as a makeshift STI clinic. The team later took a small room in Nalpak Hotel near the Rail Museum. Charu and Shahid brought in female sex workers, starting from eleven in the morning. There was a surprising trust between the female sex workers and the male sex workers and transgender people. It started as a business relationship, because there was some overlap of clients. When men approached female sex workers for anal sex, they would refer them to the MSMs or TGs, because the women invariably would not agree. If a man who came to an MSM also wanted to go with a woman, the MSM would introduce him to a female sex worker. The communities also helped each other during crises such as an illness, money problems, or violence. It was a complementary relationship, more a friendship and collegial contract, but the men were savvier. Because they had been introduced by Charu and Shahid, female sex workers were willing to talk to the team.

The team was moving around the city trying to understand where the clients and sex workers first made contact. They found that frequently there were no specific spots, but stretches of road that might be as much as two kilometres long. Within that stretch there could be several hotspots. Sushena led training programmes for the new staff, most of it in the field. One of her first recruits was K.T. Venukumar (KT), a postgraduate in social work. He would take Sushena around the city on his motorcycle, pointing out hotspots.

~

In the first week, almost thirty women were meeting regularly in the Nalpak Hotel room, and they in turn were introducing more sex workers. Some women were not introduced, but discovered by the programme. Kavita, who we will meet later, was one such woman. Of the thirty, more than half were willing to spend time with the fledgling programme. They were named community guides and asked what they thought they should be paid. After discussions among themselves they asked that they be paid the price for one client who would be lost in the four hours a day that they would commit to the programme. On that basis the salary was fixed at hundred rupees a day, a nominal amount, suggesting that the women considered the programme valuable.

The MSMs and transgenders played an important role in explaining the overlap of their sexual networks with those of the female sex workers. Understanding this overlap was important to get a clear understanding of how the virus was spreading. Raghav, an MSM, joined after ten days. He was dynamic, and with Charu and Shahid the programme now had a powerful three-man MSM force.

The community soon realized they couldn't keep working from a hotel room. It was also clear that the women didn't like to talk about programme work in the field, when they were on their own business. Finding office space was not easy, because landlords were unwilling to rent space that HIV positive people and sex workers would visit. The programme finally found a nice office space, with a sympathetic landlord. It was near a bus stop – which was a primary consideration. There was a temple and a mosque nearby, as well as a school. The headmaster of the school was a big supporter, as he considered it a nice social work project.

In those early days, every time I visited, I felt that the office radiated happiness. There was a special energy I felt as I walked up each flight of steps. On the first floor was a space of about 500 square feet, with several desks, a clinic, and a meeting room. Up another flight of stairs there was a similar-sized room, but it had no furniture at all, only durries on the floor. Many transgenders are good artists, and the walls were covered with murals. They made it look something like Tahiti, with women and children sitting on a shore, beneath coconut palms, facing a blue ocean.

~

The ICHAP team had asked for twelve weeks to get a programme under way and didn't want to fall short on that promise. Their game plan was to put the basics in place and refine things as they kept going. The idea was to gauge the size of the sex worker population in the first six weeks, and to start delivering services to prevent HIV in the next six weeks. In just a few weeks the sex workers of Mysore had a core team and an office space that came to be simply called the Drop-In Centre, while the team was getting to know more and more sex workers. On 1 January 2005, a year after the grant was made to ICHAP, they named the project Ashodaya, meaning 'dawn of hope'.

The basics had been set up. Work had to start, and the key question now was: how many people do we have to serve? How many sex workers were out there? Ashodaya worked out a unique and effective method for finding out those numbers.

13

Counting the Numbers

'Hey, when they do it with birds and fish, why not us – have you ever seen more exotic birds?' There was laughter all around. That quip captured the spirit with which Mysore's sex worker community set out on the remarkable exercise of estimating their own numbers. It was the first time they had come together to accomplish something difficult, and it was a task only they could do.

By mid-February 2004, six weeks since the meeting with ICHAP, it became crucial to start the delivery of HIV prevention services – making condoms available, treating STIs, educating sex workers about the risks of unprotected sex.[1] The poser was: how do you deliver these services effectively, if you don't know how many people to deliver the services to and how many condoms they each need?

We had seen so many HIV prevention programmes across India that blindly delivered condoms, without a clear idea of how many condoms needed to be delivered. They looked at how many patients came into their clinics, without knowing how many more patients needed to come in. There would be cans overflowing with condoms in places that got high traffic like men's latrines, while condoms would not be available in vibrant hotspots where sex work took place.

A sound HIV prevention programme has to begin by estimating

how many sex workers there are, of what types they are, how many condoms they used, and whether they were already getting their condoms from somewhere else. Linked to the number of condoms they needed to distribute, the programme could work out the number of STI treatments that would need to be given. Only then could the programme track progress meaningfully. And only a sex worker can reach and get this kind of very private information from another sex worker. This is the crux, and this is why counting the numbers had to be an exercise led by sex workers.

~

By then, besides the four or five staff members, there were about twenty sex workers involved with the programme on a part-time basis, working on a small honorarium. Of these a few were male sex workers and transgender people. There was a meeting every day of the Ashodaya staff and all the sex workers who were involved with the programme. At one of these meetings, Sushena asked how many sex workers there were in Mysore city. Hands went up, and the estimates ranged from five hundred to five thousand!

Sushena believed that certain conventional estimation methods[2] were too broad to be useful, especially with the target population moving constantly. So they decided to try out an approach that Sushena had used when she was working earlier in Bangladesh, called 'capture-recapture'. This was first used by ornithologists to estimate bird populations in a forest, and after that had been used occasionally in epidemiology. The only way it could be tried out in Mysore was if the sex workers themselves ran the process.

Sushena explained it to the group: 'If there is a fish pond and you want to know how many fish there are in the pond you first cast a net and maybe you'll catch a few fish. You mark those fish you catch and throw them back again into the pond. Then you cast a much bigger net and count how many fish you have caught the second time, and from those you see how many were from the ones you caught the first time, because they will have the mark. In this way you can find out how many fish there are in the whole pond, doing some calculation.'[3] We can do the same thing for all the sex workers in Mysore. But you have to lead it – can you? Everyone agreed, and the conversation turned to how they should go about the task. They started developing the plan together in detail.

~

A lot of preparation went into the 'capture-recapture' exercise. It was scheduled to happen on the last Saturday of January and the first Saturday of February 2004.

The sex workers divided the central part of the city into three zones, A, B, and C, keeping the Drop-In Centre as the middle point. The zones fell contiguously, in the central parts of Mysore city. In total, about sixty hotspots had been identified across these zones, counting both lodges and places in nearby open grounds.

The staff, through the community, studied precisely where sex work was happening, based on a testing of the sex traffic in the city for twenty-four hours. There were five teams of sex workers to conduct the exercise, each with a team leader. Lottery tickets were printed because they were to be a key part of the exercise.

On the first Saturday the teams gave a lottery ticket to all the sex workers they met, conducting the exercise only in one of the three zones. They told these women that there would be a lottery draw with special prizes within a month's time. They placed a mark on these tickets and on the counterfoil they retained. On the next Saturday they approached sex workers on the street – recognized easily by the team members – and offered them a lottery ticket. They placed a time stamp and a different mark on those tickets and counterfoils. If they met a woman who had already received a ticket the first time, they told her she didn't need another ticket, but made a special mark on that woman's counterfoil. It was exactly analogous to catching fish, marking them, and letting them go.

Major hotspots for sex work in Mysore, 2004

Legend
★ Hotspot
┊ Zones

ZONE A
ZONE B
ZONE C

THEOBALD ROAD
JAYACHAMA-RAJENDRA CIRCLE
BANGALORE NILGIRI ROAD
Central Bus Station
KALAMMA TEMPLE STREET
IRWIN ROAD
City Bus Station
Mysore Palace
SAYYAJI RAO ROAD
SAYYAJI RAO ROAD
DHANVANTRI ROAD
VINOBA ROAD
D. DEVARAJA URS ROAD
RAMAVILAS ROAD
CHAMARAJA DOUBLE ROAD
Mysore City Junction
IRWIN ROAD
HUNSUR ROAD
JHANSI LAKSHMIBAI ROAD

0 metre   500

Over two Saturdays, the Ashodaya team had gathered enough data to work out estimates of the sex worker population. The numbers were: 1475 female, 200–300 male, and 80–100 transgenders. They used these numbers to plan out how to deliver services. As time went by and more data came in, the staff were surprised at how accurate the first estimate had been.

A month later over a hundred women came for the lucky draw at the Ashodaya Drop-In Centre. Three prizes – all kitchen utensils – were awarded to the winners. Coffee and sweets were offered. There was an atmosphere of celebration.

~

The capture-recapture exercise yielded two important outcomes. The first was the learning that a community of sex workers could flawlessly carry out a complex task, working in teams, if they had been trained well, and empowered to make decisions in the field. KT and other Ashodaya staff say they have no doubt that if the sex workers had done the exercise again and again, they would have been able to do it with minimal supervision by the third or fourth time round and soon they would have been able to train others. The acumen that the sex workers showed, intent on doing a perfect job, their sense of ownership, and willingness to help each other out, were a revelation. The second outcome was a wave of pride and the sense of belonging to a community that the exercise created.

How did it happen that a community of sex workers, marginalized, living in dire circumstances, could carry out such an intricate task? The answer is that these women have capabilities that have been long suppressed and larger aspirations that have never found an outlet. The estimation exercise gave free rein to these qualities. It was the first time their capabilities were being recognized, and they felt respected.

~

The community of sex workers in Mysore was taking important steps together. But no community is homogeneous, it is made up of individuals. If one looks more closely at who these individuals are, there will be a better appreciation of the overall picture. One of these individuals is Kavita, a sex worker from the small town of Shimoga, not far from Mysore.

14

Kavita

I think of Avahan as a mosaic made up of thousands of small chips. Each chip is a life, the life of a sex worker who became part of a programme that became a movement. A lot can be read from each, if it is examined closely.

Kavita is a sex worker in her forties, and she is part of the mosaic of Ashodaya, the programme in Mysore that Avahan started in 2003. What was she made of? Where did she come from? How did she rise above her circumstances and make something of her life? It is important to appreciate individual lives to get a sense of the larger movement that those people built.

Even though I had known Kavita since the beginning of the Mysore programme, I knew only the broad strokes of her life. Now I asked her if she would tell me her life story in some detail, for this book. She agreed. Her words came out haltingly at first, then in a torrent. She spoke, for the most part, with complete self-control.

Kavita started in English, a language she has taught herself in recent years. As she got involved in telling her story, words failed her, and she switched to her native Kannada (KT, an Ashodaya staff member, translated). What follows is Kavita's story, in her own words.

1

My proper place is Shimoga where I was born in 1974. I lived with my mother, father, and three brothers. I was the youngest. My father worked in a textile showroom. My mother was an assistant supervisor in a BDO [Block Development Office, a government organization]. One of my brothers was a lawyer. We were comfortable. Everything was good in the family. The house had two bedrooms and a living room.

My parents were strict because we are from the Vysya community [a trader caste] that is very traditional. They never left me alone and my father or a brother would always accompany me. It's not just my family, the whole Vysya community is like that.

My school was known as National School. When I was in school I was getting a lot of support from my father and mother and even from my brothers. When I finished tenth [grade] my mother wanted to get me married. Then the principal in the school, her name was Shardamma, said why do you want to get her married, she is studying well, she is a good student too. Shardamma Principal convinced my mother and father. I studied hard, got a high first class in school, and was admitted to college.

2

In college I made a friend, his name was Raju. We were sharing books and talking about studies and so on. I was studying arts. Raju and I became very close. He told me in the first year itself that he would take care of me and we would get married.

I was seventeen. Raju was much older, maybe by four–five years. Raju was very handsome, tall, and a bit dark, and cracking a lot of jokes. He had nice eyes, sparkling! I would tell him about my problem, of my parents being strict, and he would give me proper guidance. He came from a poor background. He was from a lower caste, a scheduled caste, and that's why there was later a problem.

We were bunking college and going out to the park and to movie theatres. My interest in college was going down. The college principal realized that and called my parents to the college. She told my parents that I am not interested in studying and not coming to college. She did not say I was going with Raju because that was a secret only two of my friends who were very close to me knew. Those days, before a young girl was married, going with a boy was not accepted.

Rekha and Rupa were the two friends knowing about Raju. My mother talked separately with those friends and asked them why I am not going to college. And Rekha and Rupa told her about Raju.

When Raju was proposing, it was they who helped me, saying he is a good guy and he is loving you. After a few days, the same girl, Rekha, told me that Raju's character was not very good. That he loved another girl and in between he left her. I don't know why she told my mother about Raju. Maybe because she was very competitive with me in school. By this time I had known Raju about seven or eight months. Till that time there was no sexual relationship with him. I'll tell you that later.

Then my mother shouted at me and beat me with a stick, though she did not tell my father and brothers. When exams were over I scored very low with a third class in the first year. Then my mother said, you are not doing well and there is no need for you to go to the college. But I convinced her that I will make it up in the second year. I also convinced my father who had got to know by this time.

In my second year in college, for three to four months I was avoiding Raju. Then he started coming to my street on his bike when I was on the roof. We stayed on the first floor and I used to go up on the roof to dry clothes. He found some children to bring letters to me.

At that time, I was feeling very lonely because I had left my two friends who had been misguiding me. I was going to an English typing school in those days just near my house in the evenings. Raju started coming there. We only met like that outside the typing school. That news got to my mother. She and my father both beat me and said there was no need to go to the college. They put me into a room and locked it. For almost one month I was there in that room. Then Raju started coming and roaming about in the street and finding out from different people what happened to me. I got to know this only later.

Then it happened there was the Shivaratri festival, and in my area they used to do the temple puja the whole night. My parents had gone to the puja that night and my brothers had gone somewhere else. That time Raju sent a letter through my neighbour's small boy. In that letter he said, I am ready to marry you, and if you are ready to love me then pack a few clothes and we can run away.

After I got the letter I started thinking, okay, he understands me, and I understand him, why can't we get married? If I got married to another person, I may not like him, he may not like me. My parents used to lock the door from the outside and leave the key at the neighbour's house. I told the neighbour's boy to go and get the key and open the door. He opened it and I went down.

I packed a few clothes and had very little money, but I went with Raju and he took me to Mysore. My mother and father showed me no love. They used to beat me, and when I ran away with Raju I was feeling very angry with them. Now I feel that parents should be strict, but not to that extent.

3

When we came to Mysore he took me to his elder sister who was living with her husband – they have no children. He said to his sister, I love her and we both ran away from her house. I am going to get married to her.

One day when his sister and husband had gone out of Mysore he approached me for sex and I rejected him. I told him I would have sex only after marriage. He told me that we came here only to get married so why are you not cooperating. He was very loving to me and I agreed and it was only then we had sex. It went on for three or four months like this. Every time the sister and husband were out of the house we used to have sex. Then I started thinking, why are we not getting married, and every time he is coming only for sex. I started thinking that this time he will cheat me.

One day Raju and his sister and his brother-in-law told me their mother was not feeling well and they had to go see her. The mother's place was in T. Narasipuram, about thirty kilometres from Mysore. I said I'd also like to come. Then Raju said, look here, we are not married right now, if I take you to the village it will look bad. Once we get married I will take you. Then I was very scared as I had never been alone, and I said no, no, I cannot stay alone, and then he said, okay we will come back in the evening. But for three–four days he did not return to the house. I asked the neighbours where Raju's family village was and then I went there. The house was locked. The neighbour said he is gone, he is getting married. He was getting married to his mother's brother's daughter, this is allowed. And they were getting married in a place called Dharma Salem. It is in another district called South Kannada. When I heard Raju had already got married three days ago I was very upset and angry. I went straight to the police station. I filed a complaint of abduction.

[Kavita sobs quietly, reliving those times. She collects herself quickly, and continues.]

The next day the police called Raju's mother and brother to the station. The brother was a government employee. They said, we don't know her and even Raju doesn't know her, her character is not good. They said I was a prostitute. Whatever complaint I gave the police was not filed and they filed a complaint against me for being a prostitute and threatening their family. His brother was a very powerful person in that town because he was from a backward caste and he was a government employee.

Then the police started inquiring from me where I was from. They took the full details of my background and the address of my parents. They sent a call to them, but they did not come – only my brother came. And he told the police, when she left we considered her dead.

We don't have any relationship with her now and whatever you want to do, you do it, he said, and he walked out. When he came to the police station, I could see him but he could not see me. I was outside, looking in.

On the first day the police beat me. On the second day they had not produced me before the magistrate and they had not filed my complaint. They had locked me in the women's lockup. And the police said, now whatever you want to do you do, but don't come back to this town. The police beat me and abused me, but not sexually.

After release from the police station I came back to Mysore to Raju's sister's house. I told her all the incidents and she said, no, no, you go, otherwise I will call my brother and again he will file a police complaint. After that Raju's sister threw my luggage and all from the home. I took the luggage and came to Mysore bus stand. I was sitting there crying the whole day. I was not knowing where to go, no money. If I go to my home definitely they will beat me and throw me out, so what shall I do. That's how I was thinking and sitting there in the bus stand the whole day and meanwhile a lot of people are observing me and wondering. The police also came and asked me, why you are sitting here, why you are crying. I told them, my friends are coming, they asked me to sit here, and that's why I am waiting.

Then in the evening one lady came; she said, I have been seeing you the whole day sitting here crying, what is your problem? Then I told her the whole story. She looked like an official going for work, maybe about thirty-eight. After listening to my story, she consoled me and she said, come and stay with me, then we can make a plan. She took me to her home and then she said, look, you are educated, you can read and write, I will get you a job.

After a while one guy came – he was not very old, maybe in his twenties. She introduced me, saying he was her husband, though he looked much younger than her. They said, tomorrow morning we will take you to the place where you can work properly. I slept the whole night and next morning they came and we all went to the railway station. We got on the train and they gave me coffee and a bun. I ate that, and I slept. When I woke up I was in Mumbai.

[I ask Kavita if she wants to take a break, but she shakes her head and continues.]

4

Why have you brought me here, which place is this, I asked. I had never been to a big town apart from Mysore and Shimoga. They said, this is a big city and you will get more job opportunities here. That is why we have brought you here.

I believed them. We came to a place where there were different buildings and a lot of women standing. We stood in front of a three-storey building and they took me to the third floor and said, why don't you go and freshen up? We will introduce you to the Amma (her name was Laxamma) and she will provide you with the job. I went to freshen up, brush my teeth, and have a wash. But when I came back they were not there, they had collected money from the Amma and gone. Then the Amma told me, you should get ready and stand on the balcony. I was refusing to do that and then the girls who stayed there spoke to me. They said, look, they sold you to Amma for sex work and she won't leave you till you have repaid the money.

After that every day she told me to get ready and go for sex work. I refused for one week. She said, I will not feed you till you work. It was a three-storey building and I was supposed to stand outside on the balcony and not on the street. It was not possible to run away because there was a security guard at the entrance. Then I got introduced to a Kannada-speaking girl, her name was Lata. She told me about one guy who comes and is very popular here. He was a rough and bold type of person, and whenever a new girl was coming he would be the first to have sex with her. Lata said, when he comes he will go first to you and then you tell your story. He is the only one who can help you. When he came he took me inside the room. He was very young, maybe in his twenties, and I told him my story, and said, please sir, help me get back to Mysore. He said, Amma is very strict and she will not leave you, but I will try to convince her. He did not have sex with me. He said, only if you want to I will have sex with you, otherwise I won't have sex with you. He was a decent man. After he left me he went to Amma and said, I had sex with her and I'll take her for the evening also. Meanwhile he told me, I'll come in the evening. Don't take any clothes or luggage from here. Just put on one dress and on top of that another dress, and just come quickly with me. That evening he came with a vehicle and took me to the railway station. He gave me a ticket to Mysore and said, don't come back here. He gave me two hundred rupees and a food packet for the journey. He said, in Mysore don't show your face to that aunty who brought you here.

5

When I came back to Mysore by train I didn't want to go into the city because of the aunty, so I sat at the railway station. Then a lady came and asked what happened. She was dark-skinned but beautiful. I told her everything. Then she said, don't sit here, this place is not good, you come to my place. She took me to her house – she was staying alone in a house which is within the city but on the outskirts, in an extension area. She said she was working in an agarbatti factory. Her name was Sheela.

She used to tell me to stay at home, she would leave the house in the morning and come back in the evening, with groceries and all. We used to cook together. After a few days I was getting irritated, thinking, how long should I continue like this, eating her food. I asked her, why can't you take me to where you work, I would also like to work. Then she told me she was not going anywhere to work and that she was a sex worker. She told me she had two children who were in Kerala. They were staying with her mother because her husband had died. She said, I go back to Kerala once a month to see my children and then I come back to Mysore to earn money in sex work. I do it to take care of my family.

I thought of Sheela, how she had come to support her family, and I thought to myself, why can't I also do that? Then I took a decision that I should take this work because I need to do some earning. It was a very difficult decision.

From then on I started going with her because she was knowing many clients and she started sharing the clients with me. But for about ten days it was very difficult for me, sleeping with the client and providing sex because I didn't know all those things. I would pick up the clients on the street and take them to the lodge, about two to three clients every day.

The clients would pay two to three thousand rupees for a night because I was new to the sex work. Sheela took the money directly from the client and gave me some, depending on what the client paid. If the client gave fifteen hundred then she might give me five hundred. If the client gave three thousand then maybe she would give me a thousand. There were clients for short sessions also and they used to give five hundred rupees to Sheela and I would get two hundred rupees.

6

Then I got to know one man, his name was Siddaraju – again a Raju [she bursts out laughing at the irony]. Sheela used to tell me, he's a good guy, why don't you get married?

In the beginning he was showing a lot of love to me like the other Raju. That Raju was very black, but this Raju was very handsome and he was also white. Raju was a cook, cooking at marriages and at that time he was staying in Sheela's house. Sheela herself took us to the temple, got us married, and found a house for us, near her house.

Whenever it was the marriage season he would say, don't go for sex work, I will feed you and take care of you. When there was no work he would be in his room and drink the whole day. He had two bad habits – one was drinking and the other was single number lottery where you scratch and get the number. One day he said to me, don't feel bad, I want to ask one thing – whenever marriage season is not there, why don't you go for sex work so that we can share the earning? So I again started going for the sex work.

For six to seven months he was very supportive and very close to me. Then he started behaving very badly. He stopped going for work even in the marriage season. He would stay at home the whole day having drinks and playing lottery, and whenever I was not earning anything he would beat me. He asked, who are you giving the money to? At that time there was a lot of police problem, a lot of violence and so sometimes by the end of the day we would not have earned anything.

After that I started working from the Wesley Church opposite the bus stand. There was a group of girls who operated from the pavement in front of the church and the whole day they would be drinking. I used to pick up clients from there and take them to the lodge. I started addicting from drinks at that time. I was pregnant three months from Raju's child. I thought that if I drink more the child could be aborted.

I stopped going home because if I went back he would beat me and I started spending more and more time on the street. I was drinking more and more all through the day. At night I would sleep in the railway station.

The girls who operate from the railway station didn't have a home. They would pick up clients from in front of the church or the railway station where there was a public toilet. At night they would sleep in the railway station. They introduced me to a lot of police people. The police knew I was a sex worker and whenever I slept at the station I paid them fifty rupees.

Raju found out I was outside Wesley Church picking up clients and again he came to me and said, why don't you come back and stay with me, I won't demand money from you, and again I got convinced. I came back home, Raju started sending me in the evening for sex work, saying you go in the night and come back in the morning. The neighbours told me whenever I was going out from the house he used to bring other girls home. The neighbours and the owners told me I should vacate the house.

Again I started staying in the railway station. Three or four months it went on like that. Raju was not earning and so he started coming with me, staying with me in the railway station. I was thinking, look, I am seven or eight months pregnant, what will happen to me after I deliver, so he and I rented a room together near the station.

We six or seven women operating from Wesley Church were very close to each other. Whenever one was unable to get client they would take care of her and provide her with drinks and all that. They told Raju, look, she's eight months pregnant so don't send her to sex work, whatever money you want we will provide. They told him that we will talk to the hotel person and get you a job, she should not practise sex work because if something happens to her later you won't have any earnings. Raju became a cook in the hotel and began to earn some money.

Mani and Rajeshwari were from that group of my friends and they both later joined Ashodaya. They were very close to me. After they joined Ashodaya their boyfriends said, we are not going to pay you any more. Both girls got murdered by their boyfriends. Rajeshwari got murdered near the railway station. We made a big public case out of it and that was one of the main incidents that brought out the issue of violence publicly. That man is in jail now with a fourteen-year sentence.

Then my baby Pooja was born in the government care hospital. I had two feelings at that time. One, I was very happy. Pooja was born on a Friday and everyone said she is Lakshmi, she will bring good fortune. Apart from that I was very scared. I was wondering now who will support her.

[Kavita's eyes are shining when she talks of Pooja's arrival. It was clearly the happiest moment of her life.]

7

Raju was very happy, and I was staying again at his house. Once he was earning we shifted to [the adjacent] Mandya district because he got a job there. For six months he took care of me, but we were concerned about the baby's future. One day we sat together, and we agreed that

I should go back to sex work three days each in Mandapuram in Mandya, and in Mysore. Raju was earning five–six thousand rupees a month. I could earn two to three thousand practising only three days a week. After a few days Raju started drinking, he started beating me again, and that's why I started drinking again daily, often in the morning. We started with whisky and switched to arrack, which comes in packets.

Three–four years went by drinking and fighting. In 2003 I got friendship with Raghav, an MSM sex worker. Raghav was operating from R-Gate in Mysore and I also used to pick up clients there. Wesley Church was very close by. It was convenient, with a lot of bushes and so on, where we could hide if the police raided.

I used to bring my child to work with me then when I did sex work, because there was nowhere to leave her. Whenever I got a client I would leave the child with my friends. Raghav had a very soft corner for me because I used to bring my daughter. He used to share his clients with me. He never took any money from me.

[By that time Raghav had got introduced to ICHAP's technical team who were scouting Mysore.]

At that time Raghav introduced me to the Ashodaya technical team. He said, they want to help sex workers, why don't you work with them and in the evening you can still do sex work. I was not interested, as my mind was only on how to make money. I was drinking in the morning and not really thinking about my daughter's future at that time.

Then Raghav started falling sick very frequently. I used to admit him to the government hospital, often staying the night, spending a lot of money for his health. One day when Raghav was in hospital I met Kaveri madam and Venu sir [they were then with ICHAP but later joined Ashodaya] in the field. I met them at R-Gate. When they came I was totally drunk. They asked me if I wanted to work for sex workers and I was drunk, so I just said, okay I'll see you, and went away.

The next day also they came to the field and Sushena madam was also there. They took me to Hotel Samraj and give me coffee and all that. That day also I was drunk. They asked me if I would introduce them to my friends and I said okay. They also asked me about my personal life, how much I used to drink and so on. After that I started coming to their office. I would bring my friends. We would all drink in the morning and come, the same women who are my friends in front of the church. I used to sit with the staff and they told me drinking is bad and that I should drink buttermilk [*laughing*]. I thought, okay I will also start working here, and then I joined. This was February 2004. Before me there were already ten to fifteen members. For example, there was Bhagya and she is still here.

<h1 style="text-align:center">8</h1>

Whenever I was not drinking I would go with the team. I was needing money and I realized that in the morning I could earn from here and in the evening through sex work. They gave me a card and all. Raghav and I were very close at that time. These days I look back and think he was like my husband only.

What I liked about them was that they never talked about the work, they talked about me. That very much impressed me. But I didn't like when they told me don't drink. At that time, I had never used condoms. Out of ten clients maybe one or two would bring a condom. I had never heard of HIV and AIDS till then; it was only after I came into this programme.

In 2004 Raju was very sick. They tested him and found HIV. The doctor there was very nice, Dr Somanna, and she was very close to Sushena madam. She told Sushena madam that I also should get tested. I was very surprised why they were testing me and the counsellor explained to me. Then I was tested, and it was found that I was positive. I was totally lost. Again, I went back to the same business – drinking morning to evening. I was not coming to work. I would stay in the small tarpaulin shelter, under the tree near the church. Project people would come to me and try to convince me. I used to listen to them then do whatever I felt like. In the meantime, Raghav died and it was the project people only who came and took care of the body.

The project people identified the skills I was good in. I took the training in how to do presentations and I was practising that all the time. Then it happened that people were coming from Bill & Melinda Gates Foundation (India) and I was to give presentation. I practised all day and next day when I was to give the presentation I was totally drunk in the morning and slept in the street.

Evaluation was happening for all staff every three months. Every week there was a community meeting and questions were raised openly if a guide [Kavita was a guide, elsewhere referred to as peer worker – a practicing sex worker, working part-time on the programme] was meeting the criteria. I was demoted by the community to volunteer after a meeting. I was determined to come back to the same position. For three months I worked hard and then the community put me back to the same position of guide.

9

Then Bill Gates's father was coming to Delhi in August 2005, and for two days I was practising. They told me, please don't drink and forget. That day we were supposed to go to Delhi. Morning I drank and slept in the street. They picked me up from the street. In Delhi I practised a lot and the day of the presentation they watched me so I could not drink. [The presentation was to Bill Gates Sr, Ratan Tata, Sudha Murty, and others.] After the presentation they called us for a big dinner that night, more than two hundred people. Bill Gates's father was very happy and he called me to the stage and gave a kiss to me. He told me to sit next to him at the dinner table.

It was on that day that I realized I have a life to live and I need to change. But even then after a few days I was drinking off and on. When I had the money, I was drinking.

On 23 December 2005 Ashodaya was registered as an organization. A meeting of the community was called, about six hundred people, to select the treasurer, president, vice president, secretary, two members of the board, and so on. The criteria included not drinking at work, not picking up a client at work, listening to the community, being ready to face the media. The community chose me to be the first treasurer even though I was drinking. But I was mingling with them, not fighting with them, and supporting others, and they saw that.

After I became treasurer I made a few decisions. Like, I must admit my child to school. So with the help of the project I got Pooja admitted to the boarding school. Then I shifted myself to a rented house and started giving more time to the project. I started bringing my friends into the programme and talking to them about how we can solve our own problems. My testimonials had a lot of influence on other community members, because they knew how I was before and how I am now. Some stopped drinking, others started coming to the office. They started talking of health services and every month coming for the MHC [monthly health check-up]. People were telling I was becoming a role model.

As the treasurer I was not handling all the project money but only the small donations that came from community members, and money to vendors, and so on, about five thousand rupees monthly in the beginning. I knew how to handle a long book because I had been educated enough, so every day I would write down how much were the collections and how much was spent. Then the project people trained me how to handle a cash book. I learnt how to use the computer, only basic level, but I learnt how to use Excel and MS Word and make a simple PowerPoint presentation. I go through all the mail that comes to Ashodaya and mark events that may be coming we have to attend, and so on. I became a trainer and did many trips to foreign countries.

One day they took me and admitted me to a de-addiction centre eighteen kilometres from Mysore. I was there for a month. After coming back from there I did not drink for two to three years. Even now on occasion I only have a beer.

The entire purpose of my life changed. Till then I had thought that my life is gone, that drinking was my life.

10

Now my daughter is twenty-two. She goes to college, studying for her BEd degree. As part of her course she and some people from UN wanted to study our project. I had never really discussed my life with her so I was nervous. Friends from the project talked to her first and she said, sir, I knew all this all along, I always knew my mother was tested positive.

[Kavita's eyes well up, and she pauses to sip water, but soon continues.]

Pooja said to me, how much you suffered for me, how much pressure you took to take care of me. I remember very well those days we lived on the street together. Now it is my turn and when I finish college I will take care of you. She wants to sit for some competitive exams, she talks about the IAS.

In 2009 I met a man called Manjunath. He was positive. We knew each other for about two–three years, then he died in December 2012. We had a daughter, and she is now six years old. She is in a boarding school about sixty kilometres from here. She is also brilliant, she takes dance classes and karate classes. The school is run by an NGO and they take for free any kids who come through Ashodaya.

I often think of that young man who saved me in Mumbai and changed my whole life. If I could see him I would thank him. Sometimes when I eat, I think I owe this food to him.

11

In 2009–10 there was a project on stigma discrimination funded by the World Bank and I gave an interview that time to CNN-IBN about how we are dealing with these issues. We got an award from the ADB. When my parents saw that programme, my brother came to Mysore and said you're doing a good job. Then they started connecting with me, my mother and my brother are now in touch with me. Any time there is a function there they call me. I talk to them because of my daughter, because I wanted her to have a grandmother. But I haven't forgiven them.

Then one day my daughter spoke to them. I am not as direct as my daughter. She said to them, when my mother was in crisis you did nothing to help her. My mother told Pooja, you should forgive us, but your mother Kavita also made a mistake. Pooja said, because of that mistake my mother went to different countries and is where she is today. If she had been with you her life would have been nothing.

Whenever I talk to my daughter I try to recall the past because she should know the trouble that I have been through. Sometimes even now I have a flashback like in movies and I think from where to where have I come.

[I look at Kavita's face closely, and I can see that she was once beautiful. Today her face bears scars, and her eyes carry a sadness. Her body looks worn, and she seems weary. But her face changes in a flash, laughter comes readily, and there is an energy and radiance whenever she speaks about Pooja.]

~

[On a subsequent visit I ask tentatively, if I can meet Pooja. Kavita readily agrees. I meet Pooja alone at the Ashodaya office. She is in the final year of her BEd degree, and is an A student. She is in a printed blue salwar-kameez and has her hair tied in a loose knot. She stays in the college hostel. Pooja is a soft-spoken, personable young woman, quick to laughter. I ask Pooja to tell me about her childhood.]

My childhood memories are of Amma working all the time, and Appa never working. For a long time, we lived in half-built buildings, sleeping on newspapers. He would snatch away whatever Amma brought back in the evening from her work. He would go and get drunk, come back, and beat both of us. I still have the marks. When he died, I don't know why my mother cried. My only thought was that finally our problem had ended.

I am very fortunate to get a mother like this. She always protected me and gave priority to my needs. She never kept me hungry. Bringing back things like buns and other things, she always used to feed me first. When there was a festival or special occasion, she would get me a dress to wear when she didn't have one herself. If she didn't have money at all, she would say do you mind if I get it for you next time.

Amma told me about the difficulties of life, and how to lead a life. She told me about how people will treat you, and how you need to deal with them. She taught me what kind of different people there are and their different ways. She spoke about skills I must learn – English, computer knowledge, and general knowledge. She always said whatever we have, whatever wealth, we need to share with those who are needy. Because God will give us extra if you care for others.

Now I need to get a steady job, a government job. I need to get all kinds of facilities for my Amma so that she's never facing any difficulties again in her life. Sometimes, in the evening times, Amma and I talk about the incidents of the past. We will cry together, and we will sleep. Each step she fought and faced a lot of difficulties.

[I ask Pooja – what is the biggest quality that your mother has, and that you have got from her? Without hesitation she says one word – 'humanity'. I ask her what is the one thing that she has not been able to get from her mother, and again the answer is immediate – 'English'. Pooja dissolves into giggles.]

15

A Place of Their Own

The capture-recapture exercise in early 2004 had estimated that there were about 1500 sex workers, 200 MSMs, and 100 transgender people in Mysore. They were at high risk of getting infected by the HIV virus and had to be reached as quickly as possible. The problem was that sex work in Mysore, as in most parts of India, was almost entirely street-based. Sex workers were dispersed, moving from location to location, and tough to identify – how were they to be found?

The programme had to ensure that they would always use condoms, and that condoms were available whenever they needed them. STIs[1] had to be treated effectively (and of course there would be fewer STIs if condoms were being used). And there had to be constant communication, especially with the new entrants into the trade, about HIV and the need to use protection. Most programmes begin with awareness and condoms. At Ashodaya, the sex worker communities had stated their own priorities – a safe space, a clinic, and stopping violence – should come first. Sushena saw that they would earn the community's trust only if they respected this wish.

The safe space had already been provided in the form of the Drop-In Centre. A high-quality STI clinic had now to be set up quickly. It would also attract the many sex workers dispersed on the street like a magnet. Why was a clinic so important to a sex worker? The government hospital should have provided free health services, but it was an intimidating place for sex workers. When a nurse or a doctor in a government facility saw a woman with STI symptoms she would be stigmatized as a sex worker and treated callously. Women sex workers needed the support of a man when they went looking for treatment in government facilities, and this was often unfeasible. Consequently, sex workers would delay treatment, or they would take medication given by pharmacists without prescription, which could be dangerous. At times they went to unqualified medical practitioners or to expensive private clinics. These were the reasons why having a clinic of their own was such a pressing need for the sex workers.

~

Ashodaya developed three organization levels – staff, community consultants, and guides. These were roles that people played without hierarchy. Guides were practising sex workers who were paid to work four hours a day for the programme. They acted as the interface with the broader community of sex workers out on the streets (Kavita, who told her story in the previous chapter, was a guide). Community consultants were male sex workers who acted as coach, mentor, and manager, assigned to a group of guides, mainly in the field. They were more street savvy and were trusted by the female sex workers. They also were paid for the part-time work they did for Ashodaya. Staff were the non-community people like Sushena, KT, Kaveri, and Senthil, who acted as full-time managers of the Ashodaya programme and its organization. They looked at overall work planning, managed advocacy, provided technical support and training, and documented learnings.

There was a working partnership between male and female sex workers because sometimes they shared clients. It was an unusual symbiotic relationship that we didn't encounter in many other places. It could also be more than pure business – deep friendships existed between many male and female sex workers. This partnership between the guides and the community consultants was an important factor in estimating numbers, delivering services and, as we will see later, in fighting back against violence.

These roles were fluid, depending on the situation. Some guides who were highly experienced acted like community consultants or staff, for example, Rajamma and Mobile Pragya, whom we will meet soon. Staff often spent a lot of time in the field, working alongside the guides, following their lead, on projects like the numbers estimation. Guides, community consultants, and staff worked in units of five to six people. By mid-2004 Ashodaya had about thirty-five staff. Apart from Dr Sushena, there were two people for administration and finance, five (non-community) programme staff, three (MSM) community consultants, and twenty to twenty-five guides.

The desire to improve their own personal circumstances was what drew people into Ashodaya, but as time went by they were often found willing to sacrifice personal interests for what they saw as a common cause.

The view in Ashodaya was that sex workers best understood their own needs because they had personally experienced the many barriers that came in the way. It followed that they would have the best insights about solutions, and so the question of how to implement these solutions was also best left to them. It was common sense, and there was also no other option. The role of the staff was to support the sex worker community through training, mentoring, and advocacy. The explicit goal was to have staff become redundant, and for Ashodaya to become a strongly self-sufficient, community-based organization.

~

The Ashodaya way of working originated with Sushena, who came from the remote state of Tripura, bordering Bangladesh. Prior to Mysore, her work experience had been mainly in Bangladesh, as a young doctor with CARE from 1994 to 1998. These were formative years, when she found three good mentors, all medical doctors – Swarup Sarkar from the WHO; Smarajit Jana, the creator of Sonagachi; and Sundar Sundaraman, the psychiatrist who was now part of the team in Mysore. Sushena had done her medical training in Nagpur and earned an MPH and PhD as a Fulbright scholar after she left CARE, from the University of Alabama.

It was easy to underestimate Sushena and her chances of success in Mysore. Her work experience was no more than the few years in Bangladesh. She did not speak a word of Kannada. In fact, in general she spoke very little, though when excited, words came out in a torrent. It was then sometimes tough to understand her, because of her pronounced Bangla accent. She knew nothing about the local customs and culture when she came to Mysore. She had only recently emerged from a shattered marriage, two small children in hand.

Sushena had been through a phase in her life when she was the victim of sustained mental and physical abuse. She came from an aristocratic family, with several strong-willed and highly independent women, especially her mother. She looks back and realizes how difficult it was, even for her, to admit that she was a victim. It was this experience that gave her such a strong empathy with downtrodden women, and an intolerance for violence against them in any form.

Sushena looked a highly unlikely revolutionary – and yet she sparked the creation of a remarkable community movement in Mysore. She sowed the seed of Ashodaya and nurtured its growth, working behind the scenes, with a style that was empowering. It was leadership of the highest kind.

I ask her what was the one thing that enabled Ashodaya to develop so rapidly and she says, 'It was very simple: trust and compassion spread like wildfire. They scale up very easily.'

~

The clamour from the common room at the Drop-In Centre overwhelmed the two visitors as they stepped inside. It was a cacophony of loud arguments, shouts across the room, and shrieks of laughter. All along the walls, the visitors saw brightly painted depictions of happy scenes from imagined lives. From the small pantry came the special aroma of Mysore coffee, and sex workers in a small crowd were jostling, trying to get to the dispensing station.

Sitting cross-legged on cheap tent-house durries or slouched against the walls were about eighty members of the Mysore sex worker community. There were transgenders in gaudy saris, kothis – sathla as well as regular – and female sex workers, who were in the majority. There were the guides and community consultants, and a good number of curious street sex workers, no doubt also attracted by the hot snacks on offer. A good-looking young male sex worker with wavy hair and grey eyes was dashing around, trying to shush the crowd. He had started in a dignified way, but now he was losing it. 'Dev cheyda – for God's sake – pipe down and sit,' he yelled in Kannada. He wanted to give the visitors a good impression.

Most of the women in the room looked innocuous, as though they had stepped in after their daily vegetable shopping. A few looked like paupers who had been rescued from the street. A few others seemed happily inebriated, though drinking was strictly disallowed in the Drop-In Centre.

In a matter of weeks, the sex workers of Ashodaya had started looking at the Drop-In Centre as their own space, their real home. They had asked the staff – hesitantly at first, then more confidently – for some simple amenities, and these had been provided: two showers with hot water, mirrors, and floor-level mattresses that they could use for a nap. This meeting had been called to discuss the amenity they most wanted – their clinic.

As Sushena started to speak in a soft voice, the clamour petered out, and people moved forward to hear what she was saying. She invited the visitors to come and sit by her, facing the community audience, and introduced them as doctors who had been sent by ICHAP to help set up their clinic. She said, 'You all said you needed a clinic. Where should it be?' There was a murmuring, and then someone called out, 'Here, in the Drop-In Centre.' Heads nodded.

'I thought we could rent a room for a clinic somewhere close by,' said Sushena. Someone called out, 'Why?' Someone else stood up and said, 'This is like our home. We don't want to go somewhere else for a medical check-up.' Sushena replied, 'All right, let's have the clinic here. But no one is going to set it up for you, and it's a lot of work. Are you willing to do that with the help of the doctors here?' indicating the visitors. There were several loud cries – 'Yes!'

One of the visitors asked the sex workers what kind of doctor they would like for the clinic, adding, 'We should be able to find a good female doctor.' The immediate reply was, 'Sir, we are not saying we want a female doctor. We want someone who is namma' – a Kannada word that roughly means 'ours'. When the visitors asked them to explain, one of them said, pointing to Sushena, 'We want someone like her.'

The sex workers were taken aback at being asked to help choose their doctor. Interviews began from the next day, and it wasn't easy to find the right person. Not many doctors had applied for this unlikely position. The sex workers who were part of the interview asked questions like 'Have you ever worked with sex workers? Have you treated a sex worker? How would you feel if a sex worker came up to you?' The questions were obvious ones to ask, but the sex workers read a lot into the way the person answered. They were good judges of character.

Unable to find anyone suitable, Sushena suggested someone she knew. Dr Geetanjali was from the government system, but also did a little private practice, social work, and consulting. She offered Ashodaya three hours in the afternoon, from two to five. The treatment would be for all ailments, not STIs alone. Sushena and Geetanjali were shocked to find there were forty to fifty STI cases a day. That figure was to cross a hundred cases a day when the clinic was made full-time a few months later.

~

An unexpected problem came up with the clinic – the speculum. This is a hand-held metal apparatus that a doctor routinely uses for an internal examination when checking for STI symptoms. The sex workers felt it was disrespectful and claimed that it was painful. Women had started avoiding the clinic, refusing to have the examination. To our surprise this was in fact happening in many other Avahan locations at about the same time. It says something about how the sex workers were unwilling now to accept something they considered overtly disrespectful. A male visitor to Avahan, somewhat insensitively but quite logically, said, 'Now explain this to me – these women have sex several times a day, and not always in the nicest way, and they won't allow an object to be put into their vagina?'

One of the large new mirrors that the community had asked for was leaning against a wall, waiting to be hung on the wall. Sushena stepped out of the room, came back and asked for the mirror to be placed flat on the ground. She stepped gingerly on to it and lifted her skirt up to her knees. She asked the women to file past. 'Have a good look,' she said, laughing. 'We all have the same thing down there – there's nothing so special about yours. For God's sake, let the doctor do her job and examine it.' There was a lot of laughter, and the story got around. Resistance to the speculum evaporated.

After a few months complaints started about Dr Geetanjali. The sex workers felt she lacked empathy and a 'human touch'. A community that a few months ago was afraid to look a doctor in the eye felt so empowered now as to demand that the doctor be fired. Sushena didn't think the doctor was bad, and she knew how tough it would be to find a replacement. But when the sex workers continued to be adamant, she went along. The new person they found, Dr Raghavan, quickly took charge, but his real asset was that the sex workers liked the way he related to them.

~

For sex workers going to a clinic, there was always the fear of being identified and stigmatized. Also, the rumour that she had visited an STI clinic might be planted by a competitor and reach clients. The idea that the sex worker might have HIV would turn away clients and hurt her business. STI clinics had become associated with debilitating illness. That negative perception had to be made positive, and harmful competitive behaviour had to be stopped. The staff had a lot of discussions with the community, who began to understand that it was okay to go to the clinic even when well. They had started appreciating the notion of preventive health. When this messaging went around, it brought a huge number of footfalls to the clinic. Dr Raghavan had a slogan on his wall in Kannada: 'Tell your friends, bring your friends'.

The staff had been noticing a smaller group of people who had much greater influence on their peers. They were natural leaders, who immediately commanded respect. I've seen this in almost every sex workers' group – some immediately stand out. The staff found that if they worked with that smaller group first, others became willing, and word spread faster. There were five such people. These included Neelamma, the woman Sushena had grabbed hold of during the police raid; Sundari, the beautiful one who had been raped in Chamundi Hills by the police; and Mala, who had been kicked in the stomach by her husband when she was pregnant. There was also Kavita, who had been picked up from the streets, destitute. All had experienced life-changing moments with the programme.

~

Even as the clinic was being built, the condom distribution part of the programme got under way. The male sex workers were of course the most knowledgeable about condoms. Charu demonstrated the right way to put on a condom, using a wooden penis model. He used it to show how to put a condom on to a client's penis using only the mouth. The idea was to introduce the client to the notion of the condom as giving pleasure rather than interfering with it.

Several women complained that clients would secretly puncture the condom or pull it off before ejaculation. Those men believed it was good karma for the semen to go into the vagina. One of their solutions was to tell the client, 'I'll allow you to play with my breasts when we have sex,' and they would hold him tight, so his hands weren't free to damage or pull off the condom.

As Ashodaya expanded, and more data came in, they found that 85 to 90 per cent of sex work in Mysore was in the three zones that Ashodaya had identified and focused on. Further, 80 to 90 per cent of sex work in the district happened in Mysore city itself. When the staff came up with these numbers, community members would laugh and say that they knew this all along.

~

We had asked all our implementing partners in Avahan to take up outreach services. This meant reaching the larger communities of sex workers out in the streets to provide condoms, get them into STI services, and talk about safe sex practices. The challenge across all the states we worked in was how to zero in on the sex workers who were most at risk. Many of our partners in different states were coming up with innovative methods.

Our job was to transfer best practices across the Avahan programme. We brought all our implementing partners, and their core teams, together every other month to share learnings. Ashodaya learnt from

other programmes, and implementing partners from other states had
already started visiting Mysore.

~

We developed a manual called 'Avahan's Common Minimum
Programme',[2] which laid out the norms that all our partners were
required to meet. One was to achieve a ratio of forty workers to a single
outreach worker. It was a fairly arbitrary number and we asked our
partners to treat it only as a guideline and come up with the ratio that
best applied to their local situation. With some partners, achieving the
ratio required a lot of pressure from us. The Ashodaya staff introduced
the use of sexual network diagrams to identify and prioritize individual
sex workers. A sunflower symbol, denoting a guide such as Kavita,
was drawn at the centre of a large piece of chart paper. If Kavita knew
ten sex workers directly, circles with their names were connected to
her sunflower symbol by hard lines. If she knew four others more
indirectly – meaning through an intermediary – they were connected
to Kavita, by dotted lines.

Kavita would then approach Susheela (one of her ten) and ask her
to do the same exercise for her network. Susheela's hard-line contact
would become Kavita's dotted-line contact. As Kavita did this for
each of her ten, a network began to appear. The exercise was repeated
till Kavita had up to sixty direct or indirect contacts – which was
considered the largest portfolio any guide should handle.

The next step was to categorize these sex workers for risk. These
names were listed vertically on chart paper. Many sex workers were
illiterate, so they devised symbols for types of risky behaviour. For
example, a bottle would denote that the sex worker had an alcohol
problem; a condom with an X over it said she practised a lot of
unprotected sex; many male faces indicated she saw a lot of clients;
an open palm that she faced domestic violence. These symbols were
placed in the topmost row of the chart paper.

Check marks were placed against each of Kavita's sex workers. If someone had a husband who beat her, saw many clients, and rarely used condoms she was a highest at-risk person. Kavita might zero in on ten such individuals and would meet each one twice a week, starting with those who were her direct contacts. There might be twenty at the next risk level (only one risk factor) and she would meet them once a week. Everyone else was lowest risk and she would meet them once a month. Kavita used a weekly visit calendar prepared in this way. We called it microplanning, and it was being done in different ways across Avahan.

At McKinsey I had done some work in sales force effectiveness. In effect, Ashodaya was also using a sales force. The difference was that the consumers here were invisible and moving around, and the salespeople were almost all illiterate. It was orders of a magnitude more complex, and a solution more sophisticated, than the situation faced by any business sales force I had seen.

~

Natural leaders were emerging as the programme moved forward. Many had joined in the most desperate of personal circumstances, and their leadership had blossomed slowly. Their life stories, whether female or male sex worker, are indeed often stranger than fiction. One such story is that of Shahid, the MSM I had first met on my first visit to Mysore.

16

Shahid

Shahid Pasha much prefers his community name, Husna. He has this name (it means beautiful in Urdu) perhaps because of his eyes, which are an unusual grey-blue. His slightly wavy hair is lightly oiled and combed carefully, wafting a faint scent of rose attar. He has an unusual expression, as though he is always on the verge of a smile, and a rapid-fire, earnest way of talking. He carries an air of quiet dignity. His eyelashes are outrageously long, curling upwards. I say, 'Shahid, tell me those aren't for real!' He blushes slightly and nods his head. 'In fact, sir, I have to keep trimming them.' He is altogether an unusually good-looking fellow.

Shahid has been with Ashodaya since its start and is today a pillar of the organization. Early on, he became the de facto captain of all the outreach teams, and the chief organizer of internal organization meetings and external events. Today he is director of programmes for Ashodaya, travels regularly to Africa, helping HIV prevention programmes in Kenya and South Africa work in partnership with affected communities. He has spoken of his experiences at numerous AIDS convenings in Asia and Europe.

Shahid's has been a remarkable progression since that day in December 2003 when the Ashodaya team found him broken, in a

221

frenzy of despair, at Mysore's City Bus Stand. He had recently been
diagnosed as HIV positive and was sick with worry that he had passed
on the virus to his wife, and that she in turn may have passed it to
their fourth child, to be born in a few weeks.

I had come down to Ashodaya in November 2017 to interview
Shahid for this book. Shahid has the same good looks today but he
has put on a lot of weight and carries a huge belly. I kid him about
it and ask what happened to his slim figure. 'It's because of ART,'
he says pathetically. 'Don't believe a word of it,' calls out one of his
colleagues who overheard. 'He just likes to eat Mapila biryani,' a rich
dish favoured by Shahid's wife's community.

Both of us are sitting in the quiet room upstairs in the Ashodaya
Community Centre. I ask, 'Shahid, I've never understood how you, a
kothi sex worker, are happily married with four children. I hear your
eldest daughter is getting married soon – congratulations!' His native
language is Kannada, but for my benefit he tells me his story in Urdu,
which I can follow. The words flow easily, but here and there I get the
feeling Shahid is holding something back.

~

Shahid was born in Mysore in 1972, into a family that he says was
middle class, but seems to have been abjectly poor from the way he
describes their circumstances. He had three younger siblings, two
sisters and a brother. 'There were times when we had to stay hungry,
missing one or even two meals. My father was an auto driver, a small-
time person. When he was at home we had enough money to get along
from his daily earnings. But he would leave us and go away from time
to time, for days, sometimes for a week or two, and once for almost
three months. Looking back, I think there must have been another
woman in his life.'

Shahid's father's disappearances grew longer and longer. During
one of those very long absences, the family became impoverished.

From Shahid's description, it seems like his mother had fallen into a deep depression. Once a lively young woman, she was hollow-eyed, listless. She had been talking increasingly about all of them jumping into the river to end it all.

Shahid was twelve years old. He knew they were in a hopeless situation, but the suicide idea scared him. He stepped up and announced that he would take care of everyone from then on. 'I was a kid, but felt I had a responsibility to my family,' said Shahid.

~

'I got a job selling agarbattis for an agarbatti factory. They picked up stumps of used agarbattis and brought them to a small shed where they made a paste out of them to make new sticks. They would add cheap perfume to the agarbatti sticks and resell them as new. If I sold two hundred rupees worth of agarbatti packets, I would get thirty rupees from the owner of the factory. In those days that was a lot of money and we could eat two meals with that.'

Shahid had stopped going to school as he was selling the incense sticks all day, and his mother didn't ask questions. Perhaps the dark clouds were lifting from her mind.

Someone told Shahid that truckers always bought agarbattis. Shahid started selling agarbatti packets at the truck stop, and sales were good. The truckers would buy them to place before the pictures of their gods on the dashboards of their trucks. They used the incense sticks for the puja they performed before each leg of their journey. The truckers would sometimes give him loose change if he got tea or snacks for them from nearby kiosks.

One day one of them asked Shahid if he would like to come up and sit inside the truck. 'He put me on his lap and let me hold the steering wheel. He touched me affectionately, here and there, but never in a bad way. I felt there was something wrong, but I also didn't mind,' said Shahid. It went on like this, occasionally being touched and fondled

by this trucker, or a few others like him. They paid him extra money
for the agarbattis. I ask if there was any sex, oral or anal, and he says
there never was.

Shahid goes on: 'Ever since I was small, I didn't want to play with
the boys. I liked the girls' company. I liked to cook in the kitchen and
play with dolls. When my mother was out, sometimes I would try on
her saris. Some years went by and my father had been hearing about
my girlish ways and he was angry and embarrassed, because people
were laughing.

'He finally took me to Jaipur and left me with my aunt. I was about
sixteen then, and it was the summer school break. My studies were off
and on in any case. There it started again. I made friends who were
like me, and we would hang about the circle near Hawa Mahal, to
get picked up. The men often were salesmen in town for a short time,
or tourists. There was never any real emotional relationship. I was
getting paid for short times, and sometimes for all-nighters. On good
days I even made a thousand rupees, and I had plenty of cash for the
first time. I came home after a few months, and later my father got
me a job working in a small tyre repair shop. The owner knew I was
a kothi. He and some of his friends took advantage of me. The owner
was refusing to pay most times.

'My sister got married, the one that was the older of my two
sisters. Marrying off my sister cost my father about one lakh rupees.
He probably had some money hidden away, or maybe he borrowed.
We were all happy. A few years later, when I was twenty-two, my
father told me we must get your [other] sister married. I had been
earning decently from sex work, though I hid it from my family.
But I didn't have anything like one lakh rupees, because I had also
been supporting my brother's studies. But my father had a plan. "We
will get you married first. That way we will have the dahej from the
girl, to use for your sister's marriage," he said. I went along, thinking
this was the solution to the problem. I badly wanted to see my sister
married. It was also a question of my family's honour. There was one
proposal we tried, for a girl from Kerala, but the girl's family rejected

it. Then the same family came back and said that they were ready. My family asked for one lakh, which we then reduced to seventy-five thousand. The girl's family said they couldn't afford that and could give sixty thousand. This was a big amount of money for us for my sister's wedding, so we went ahead.'

~

It would be a mistake to think of Shahid simply as a gay man who got paid for sex. His sexual identity was far more complex. As occasion demanded, he would dress in drag, with moustache shaved and eyebrows plucked, looking like a beautiful woman. He was comfortable donning a burkha, so he could move about freely, face covered. He claims that he even had sex on a few occasions with the drunken client not realizing Shahid was not a woman. He had become an accomplished classical dancer who performed onstage on special occasions. He was part of a close-knit network of kothis and transgender people in Mysore who followed a certain code of honour. He had trust-based business relations with brokers, one of whom he described as 'like my God'. He consorted with happily married men, who also lived secret lives. Husna was real, and Shahid was a mask.

The idea of entering a conventional marriage, thrust upon him so suddenly at the age of twenty-two, created an inner turmoil. Shahid says, 'I never had a relationship with any girl except of a sisterly kind, or as playmates. I never felt any kind of sexual attraction. But I had resolved that I would do whatever it took so my sister could get married. I wasn't thinking then whether my marriage was right or wrong, or how I would handle it. But I was worried sick as to how I would perform after the wedding. I feared that I could never father children, because I was not really a man.'

At the same time, Shahid was ashamed to discuss his state of mind with anyone. A well-meaning elder, respected as a maulvi, took him aside one day and said, 'Look Shahid, I know you well. The fact is you are like a girl in every way, the way you sometimes behave, talk, and walk. What will you do if you get married? You may be ruining some girl's life – just think about it before you do anything.' Shahid got angry with the maulvi. 'I felt he was not a good man, just an old budha who spent his time poking his nose into everyone else's affairs. I said, "What right do you have to say all this to me? Have you ever slept with me?"'

Shahid continues, 'I spoke to a client of mine and asked him what I should do. He told me there is nothing to get that worried about. He told me there are other kothis also who got married, and that I could always leave her if I wanted to, after getting married. This put me a little at ease. I also thought to myself that in one way it was good that the girl I was to marry speaks a different language and comes from a different place. My mind was all mixed up.' Shahid went ahead and the papers for the marriage were made ready.

Then, days before his marriage there was a calamity. Shahid had a peculiar relationship with his boss, the owner of the tyre factory. They used to have occasional sex when Shahid started work at the factory years back, but then Shahid had refused when it was clear that the boss had no intention of paying. Now, seeing Shahid getting ready for a straight marriage, something snapped inside the boss. He claimed a tyre was missing from the shop and said that either Shahid or one of his clients must have stolen it. It was a trumped-up charge, but Shahid was fired. Making matters worse, Shahid had been depending on an advance of three months' salary – 20,000 rupees – which he urgently needed for the marriage. This was a week before he got married.

~

Shahid talks about his marriage: 'My wife's name is Fareeda, and those days she was not very attractive. She was plump and had no idea about things like dress or make-up. She was an extremely simple and innocent person. She came from a tiny little town, almost inside the forest, in Wayanad, Kerala. Her father ran a tea shop. According to convention, she had to change her name after marriage, but I said that was not necessary. The marriage happened in her home town. There was no festivity. We simply went to the mosque and went through the rituals. They were very poor. She had four siblings and she was the eldest.

'When we came home I was really in a mess. That entire first night I spent wondering what I was supposed to do with her. I couldn't even talk to her because our languages were different. Two days went by like this and we had no sex. We communicated a little bit in Tamil, a language we both knew some words in. After four days she went back home, as was the custom. We still had not performed sex. I spoke to a friend of mine who was already a father. He counselled me how to go about it, how to keep my mind somewhere else, and shut off my emotions. He gave me some Ayurveda tablets as well.

'After that I went to Wayanad. It is a beautiful place, I had never seen anything like it, thick green forests, rainfall, and mountains. We took a bus to the wild animals' reserve and for the first time I saw elephants and even leopards. We went to Edakkal caves, which have drawings thousands of years old. She was no longer shy with me and was showing off as though all this belonged to her. I spent almost two months with Fareeda. We were living like man and wife there. For the first time I wasn't thinking at all that I was kothi or a sex worker.'

Shahid and Fareeda went back to Mysore together. He got into selling fruit on the road, using a new thela that he bought for five thousand rupees. In a day he earned anything from three hundred to six hundred rupees. It was a difficult business because the fruit could go bad or the rates would fall. He had been earning good money as a sex worker before marriage, but after getting married he couldn't carry on with that any more, and they were barely surviving.

~

Shahid continues, 'In the third month after we married, Fareeda became pregnant. She went back home to Wayanad for the delivery – that was the custom. I thought I can't practise sex work now in Mysore as everybody would know the situation. So I went off to Mumbai where I had friends and got into the sex work circuit. I made money. After the baby was born, I came back home and lived another six or seven months with my wife and we were like husband and wife again.'

After this Shahid started going out of town on a regular basis, whenever Fareeda went home. Her absences could be for a few weeks, or for several months. The longer absences happened four times, each time they had a child. They had three girls and a boy between 1998 and 2004. Shahid says, 'I had absolutely no idea that there was something like family planning, in those days. The first time I heard about a condom was in 2004, from Ashodaya.'

In those six years, Fareeda would have been away at her home in Wayanad for more than two years. During her times away, Shahid was earning at least a thousand rupees a day, once again.

He says, 'I went to different cities – Mumbai, Hyderabad, sometimes Pune. I had friends in every place. I would stay with them and give them some of my earnings, or sometimes just sleep on the pavement or in the railway station. Sometimes there would be fights – for example, when somebody would steal from me. But all that was part of my life as a sex worker and I was familiar with it.'

~

Shahid describes how his wife found out about his secret life: 'One time, however, when my wife came back from her home in Kerala, she was looking closely at me. She said, "What is wrong with your face, there is a change. Where are your eyebrows? Why did you shave your moustache? There is no hair on your body. You look like a girl – what have you done?" She started getting angry. I made some excuse. She still did not catch on, she was very innocent.

'When she was there at Mysore I could do a couple of clients very quietly. But she had no idea. Then it happened that I got an STI and I was in agony. For a week I stayed at home untreated, then I had to go to the government hospital and get a VDRL[1] test done. They admitted me and said you must get your wife tested also.

'She came out negative because I'd not had much sex with her in all that time. When we came home she took good care of me, even applying ointment on my wounds and all that. But she had started getting some doubts. She said you are up to something, don't hide it from me. She told this to me in a very loving way, not in anger. But when I refused to tell her anything she got angry and stormed out of the house.

'It happened once that I had brought a client home. Fareeda had gone to my mother's house, which was some distance away, for dinner. She changed her mind about eating there and packed all the dinner in tiffin carriers and came home so that we could share the food together. My wife pushed the bedroom door open and caught both of us naked in bed. She dropped everything she was holding in her hands and screamed at the man to get out of the house. We didn't speak to each other for an entire day. I couldn't get myself to say anything.

'Then she cried a lot and said, "Look what you have done to me!" I said, "Fareeda I must do this to earn some money – how do we get along otherwise? I must take care of you and the children as well. I even have a responsibility to look after my mother and father. You know I was earning nothing from the business."

'She said, "People have been telling me all this time about your ways, but I never believed them and had full trust in you. There is a limit and that is this. You must decide now which way you go." She said that we should get an operation so that we don't have any more kids. But we didn't. Time passed, and she became pregnant again for the fourth time.

'Neither of us could leave. If she went home, she would be a burden as she had two younger sisters already not married. I didn't want to abandon my family, leave my children. She couldn't leave the children with me because I couldn't take care of them on my own.

'I can't remember if it came out bit by bit or if I told her suddenly, but I told her everything. I told her how I used to go to Mumbai to practise sex work and make money. Bit by bit she began to understand and to accept.

'When she was pregnant for the fourth time she said, "Look, I'll go home and deliver and get the operation done after that, so we don't have any more babies." When she was away it happened that I attended some meeting where I learnt about HIV and it occurred to me that I have a responsibility to my wife and children. I had been having so many clients over the years. There were even days when I had ten to fifteen.

'While she was away, I got tested for HIV and the result was positive. I was sick with worry, whether Fareeda was also positive, and if she had passed on the HIV to the unborn child, or before that to any of my children. It was at this time that I met with the Ashodaya people – in December 2003. Our baby was born in January 2004, and in April I called her back. I had decided I would take her to get tested.

'The day I took her to the government hospital for the test, she kept asking me, "Why are you bringing me here, what is this about?" Our four children were with us, one newborn, and the others two, five, and seven years old. Again, she kept asking, "Why are you having me tested, why?" I couldn't meet her eyes. I said, just go do it for me, just go.

'I watched her walking in to the test room with one baby at her breast and two little children with her, not knowing why she was going. I was sitting under a tree with the other child, and something broke inside me. As I thought about her innocence, and of those children, I felt filthy. I wept and wept. I said to myself, I am a sinner. If my wife and children turn out positive it will be the greatest sin of all.'

The test came out negative in the afternoon. Shahid breaks down and struggles to compose himself.

~

I ask Shahid whether over time his relationship with his wife became one of hatred or one of love. He says, 'More than love, it became friendship.' Indeed, words like love and friendship are so often used loosely, as though love is the greater. For Shahid and Fareeda to traverse such unusual ground and arrive as true friends is a miracle.

'We are husband and wife, but our relationship is not sexual. But it is much closer than that of two friends. It is difficult to describe. We quarrel at times and then even though I don't want to I must appear very forceful and manly and put her down. Just to play my role I scream and shout at her. I must do that in front of the children especially, to show them I am the husband and I am the man of the house. If I don't do that the children will be confused. It is very different in the regular MSM community. When he comes home it's sort of like – all right let me get dinner ready. The MSM plays the woman's role.

'Sometimes when I really get angry I scold Fareeda, giving the typical handclap that comes naturally to kothi-hijras. She just came to accept my mannerisms, my customs. She decided she is not going to make fun of me or be angry with me about those things. It had no impact on our relationship. She really knows me.'

I ask Shahid whether for Fareeda this is an arrangement of convenience, there being no other option. He shakes his head.

'The fact is that as many years as I can live I want to live with her, and as many years she can live she wants to live with me. She is everything for me. To tell the truth, I don't know what she sees in me.

'When I was tested positive, and we had four children, I told her, "Look, Fareeda, my life is very fragile, and I may go any time. My life is over. You're still young and you have life ahead of you so let's do one thing, if you don't mind. I'll give you talaq. You get married again and leave the kids with me, I'll take care of them. Whatever I have got so far you take it, and I'll earn for the children. No one is going to object, I guarantee you – not my family or yours. I'll even get you married myself. I don't want to feel now that because of me everything has been lost for you."

'She said, "Look, before I got married it had never crossed my mind as to who you are, what you do, or when you do. I just said we are life partners. So to me we are life partners. If you're alive, I'll also be alive. The children are ours together. We have four children, and you as you are it is enough for me." After that I was ready to do anything for her. I was ready to fall at her feet.'

Shahid breaks down crying.

'The greatest quality in Fareeda is that she accepted me for what I am. The other is that if I must deal with someone who's needy during my work, she is more concerned than I am. She is very keen that I do something to really help that person. She'll cook even at two in the morning if I show up with a bunch of people from Ashodaya. She just loves me a lot.'

I sense that Shahid can go on for a long time about Fareeda, and I gently guide our conversation down another aspect of his life that I want to try and understand.

~

'What about your children? Do they know everything?' I ask. Shahid nods and says, 'The neighbours know about my sexuality, so too my family, and a lot of people. As they grew up I didn't want the children to get very confused, as they hear things, they get teased in school.' One day, Shahid sat his children down and explained it to them gently, and seriously.

'I said, "When I was just a little child, I felt like a girl, not a boy. *Main kya karoon – mera bhawana hi aisa hai* [What can I do, my nature itself is like that]. I did what I had to, to take care of you. I am your father." I think they accepted that was how it was. It's not as though we talk about this all the time. It's understood.

'One day we were passing a group of hijras. My son, who is very mischievous and cheeky, said, "Look, Papa, your friends are over there. How come you don't talk like them, clap your hands in that funny way." I said, "I was trying all this time to teach you not to make fun of others because they are different," pretending my feelings were hurt. So it became something we started taking lightly and even laughing about sometimes.'

I ask Shahid whether he has ever had a relationship of love with any man. He shakes his head. 'No, it was always a commercial relationship,' but he looks a bit shifty. Sushena, who had been listening quietly to the last part of our discussion, says, 'Really, Shahid? What about [she, mentions a couple of names].'

Not meeting our eyes, he says, 'There was one relationship when I was very young which I thought was real and he even took me to the mosque and put a ring on my finger, but my parents came to know and broke it up forcefully. Another one was with a man who was totally crazy, and there was also the imam. I'm still a sex worker, but it's much less. If I go once a week there will be four or five clients on that day. No all-nighters, the maximum is till two in the morning.'

I am struck by how smoothly Shahid can switch his discourse between his two lives.

~

At the end of my interview sessions with Shahid in 2017, I am very keen to meet Shahid's family, but don't want to intrude. I have heard his eldest daughter is getting married in a month. I ask hesitantly. Shahid's response is immediate: 'My family would be overjoyed to meet you, please do come.'

We drive across Mysore to Kalyangiri Nagar, a middle-class part of town, and a predominantly Muslim area. On the way, he says that he lives in a house his father bought for him. I ask how his father did that, because in the story of his childhood that he had related to me, his father was a no-good character. He says enigmatically, 'He went for Haj and came back changed. He says namaz five times a day now. Besides, he invested in real estate and managed to do really well for himself.'

We walk towards Shahid's house. The neighbourhood is clean, and small children play galli cricket with abandon, creating a racket. Shahid takes me first to the house next door, on the first floor, which belongs to his brother. He is obviously better off, judging from the brand-new large flat-screen TV in the living room, and soft furniture with plastic covering still on it, as many middle-class people are wont to do with new things. I pay my respects to an elderly woman who appears. I am puzzled as to why we stopped at his brother's house, till I realize that Shahid simply wanted to show me that his family is doing well.

We leave within a few minutes for Shahid's house, and the first thing that strikes me is the smell of freshly painted walls. The entire house is being done up for the coming wedding. The exterior is mustard yellow, with a broad deep pink and green border. It looks very attractive. Inside, most of the furniture has been taken out for the painting job. A small sofa and a couple of chairs have been brought in for my visit. The sun streams in through the curtainless windows.

Two young women come out and greet me. They are Shahid's daughters. Lubna, twenty, is the one who is to be married. The other is Ashiana, eighteen, and she is studying at university. They are both beautiful, having inherited Shahid's good looks. Both are poised, and fluent in English. Lubna is getting married very young, and it is an arranged marriage. She seems reconciled to it, saying, 'Papa was keen that I get married right away, and he set up this match. He seems like a nice boy. I want to apprentice first, and then do fashion design, and he says that's fine with him.' Ashiana (named after Ashodaya) tells me that she wants to finish her studies and then become a teacher. Shahid tells me their youngest daughter and son are away in school.

Fareeda comes into the room. Her hair is loosely covered with a dupatta, and she is wearing a simple salwar-kameez. She exudes a quiet dignity and has a hesitant smile that slowly lights up her face. We speak in Malayalam, which is my mother tongue as well as hers, though I am quite bad at it. The girls join in because they have learnt the language from their mother. We exchange pleasantries. Fareeda asks if I will come for the wedding, and I make my excuses.

Shahid leans over and whispers something to Fareeda in Kannada, in a low voice. I can make out he is saying that I want to hear about their life, about his being HIV positive and all those things. I interject and tell Fareeda there is no need, and that I had come just to get introduced to them. Fareeda says to me, 'He takes his ART regularly, twice a day.' It is her subtle way of communicating that she knows all that she needs to know and let's leave it at that.

I take leave of Shahid's family, with Fareeda saying that the next time I visit I must stay longer and bring my wife. I feel a warm glow as we drive away.

'Shahid, you told me your wife was plump and very plain – she is nothing like that. Why did you say that?' He says, 'Sir, she has changed herself completely. She used to look very homely, look at her now, after four children. She was very innocent, now she is worldly-wise – too much so.' He laughs out loud.

~

As we drive back Shahid says, 'Without my family I would be nothing today. From 2004, my life changed with Ashodaya. I have the right now to speak to people and give them advice based on my own experience. I have the right to say – what you're doing is wrong, you must use a condom. Nobody is born knowing everything. People gather learning bit by bit. Some learn quickly, some learn more slowly. But the most important thing is that at any point in time you must have someone you can share with and talk about your problems. Don't suffer your problems on your own.'

17

Fighting Back

We were shocked to find that violence against sex workers was rampant in every town in which Avahan operated. Wherever sex workers practised their trade, they were being beaten, maimed, raped, and tortured. They were attacked by the boyfriends who lived off their earnings, the goons who looked on them as prey, and the police who were sworn to protect them. That is why in Mysore they had said, 'If you want us to work with you, put an end to this violence.' We were hearing this everywhere in Avahan.

But violence against sex workers seemed to be a pervasive societal evil, and it was not within our capability to change society. I started out giving a stock response: 'But we are here to stop HIV, we can't work on violence!'

Slowly it dawned on us that violence and unprotected sex were closely linked – if a drunken client didn't want to use a condom he might well beat the woman up to have his way. Violence also made sex workers wary of participating in HIV prevention. Why would a sex worker risk revealing her identity by joining a programme when word might spread about her identity, and make her a target? Why would sex workers go around in the open, distributing condoms to other sex workers, when they might be attacked? In the beginning, sex workers wanted to stay away – or just take the condoms and disappear into the night. It was becoming clear: violence had to be contained if sex work was to be safe from HIV.[1] And who best to give us the solution but the community itself.

~

In the growth of any movement, there are usually some incidents that bring things to a breaking point. Several such events happened close to each other in Ashodaya around the summer of 2005.

First there was Mala, the woman who aborted when she was seven months pregnant because she was kicked in the stomach by her boyfriend. There was Sundari, who was raped by the police in Chamundi Hills. Then a sex worker, Lalita, was picked up on the street by the police and hauled away, while her two small children watched helplessly. Sex workers everywhere were outraged that such things could happen in public places. Even worse, that the perpetrators were free to repeat their monstrous crimes, because they were never charged.

By then Ashodaya's Drop-In Centre had been running for a year. Condoms were being provided and awareness being built, focusing on the women most vulnerable to HIV. There was a high-quality clinic that treated over fifty patients a day, and where sex workers helped out as nurses and aides to the doctor. The processes of registering Ashodaya and holding elections – to be described soon – were under way. All this was a huge boost to the self-esteem and confidence of the sex worker community in Mysore. There was a growing feeling that they could take on big tasks, for themselves, by themselves, with just a little help.

But the violence continued unabated. Outside the safe shelter of the Drop-In Centre, individual sex workers were being abused, often by groups of men. With each such incident, the long-suppressed anger within the community was inching closer to boiling point.

For Sushena, each incidence of violence against women was like an attack on her person. It opened a wound that had never healed – the mental torture and physical violence she had endured in her own life.

Then things started changing. There was no grand game plan that was envisaged and executed to perfection. The solution unfolded slowly, revealing the way ahead, with one thing leading to another. There were two parts to the solution. First there was an organic response by individuals, then by groups of women, physically fighting back, that led to the creation of a more formal crisis response system. The second part was systematic advocacy with the police, based on hard data that the sex workers were collecting.

~

Mobile Pragya is plump with smooth, dark skin, and like many sex workers in Mysore looks like any other middle-class woman. She has strikingly white teeth, and one tooth in front is slightly crooked, giving her a permanently mischievous look. Her eyes have a certain sparkle and she is prone to laughing as she talks, especially when she gets to the grimmer parts of her tale. She radiates confidence and charisma. She speaks in a rush, and I need to cut her off at times, to let KT do the translation, and to interject a question.

'My name is Mobile Pragya, but I'll tell you later why that name. In those days boyfriends used to beat us if we didn't bring them enough money in the evening. They would say, "Oh-ho, you have got another boyfriend, is it?" This was the situation for all of us. The rowdies would take us away by force, keep us locked in the house for a few days. Sometimes if the policemen saw us in the field they picked us up. They would abuse us in the police station. In those days I hated all men, because I thought all men would approach me only for one reason, to have sex.

'Once I was arrested along with some women. We were in the lockup, all waiting for the worst things to start. Before anything could happen, a nice man came with a card and we were released. I had been hearing about this new project, and how they gave women a card and no one bothered them. I decided that I also must get a card.'

~

The deputy commissioner of police (DCP) for Mysore, Vipin Gopalakrishnan, had rounded up all the sex workers his force could find in the city and thrown them in jail, before his meeting with Sushena. He had thought she was from some highly connected organization that was out to end sex work. Before she could speak he said, 'Madam, I can't lock these women up every time you come here. They too are people. It is not fair.' Sushena explained that she too didn't want sex workers put in jail, and that she was from a programme that worked to keep sex workers and the public safe from HIV. When she introduced the two women with her as sex workers, he looked surprised that they both could come and sit confidently before him.

The DCP offered tea and asked a lot of questions. His expression darkened as he learnt of the extent of violence that the sex workers of Mysore faced from the police. Suddenly, he put up his hand, and stopped Sushena mid-sentence. He called in his aide and gave orders that identity cards should be issued immediately to every worker on the Ashodaya programme – and he would personally sign each card. Sushena told him, praying he wouldn't take back his decision, that many of those workers were in fact active sex workers. He said it didn't matter.

The incident again proved what I had discovered throughout my time with Avahan – that a single good person in a position of authority could make a big change in an otherwise rotten system. Gopalakrishnan's support, in the form of a simple card, did not end all police violence or stop them from looking away when it happened. But it was a huge message – that sex workers are also citizens with rights.

It was an incentive for people like Mobile Pragya to join the programme in huge numbers. The sex workers who were given identity cards were highly protective of their cards. They recorded every incidence of violence and gave a monthly report to the police.

Vipin Gopalakrishnan was transferred to Bangalore a year later. Tragically, he died a few years later of cancer, an untimely death in his early thirties. But he had done his good work before he left.

~

Mobile Pragya continues: 'Those days I used to go to Lalitha Lodge at ten in the morning and go back home by five. It was like my office,' she says laughing. 'Sometimes the police would come around eight-thirty at night and arrest all the girls in the lodge. At that time, I had a mobile phone and so the lodge people used to call me Mobile Pragya. I was the only such person with a phone. When the police raided they would arrest everyone but not me. There was a feeling that since I had a mobile I must be having contacts. I started being well known for that.'

One day the Lalitha Lodge owner got a message that the sub-inspector of police wanted to see 'Mobile Pragya' at the police station. There Mobile Pragya was accused of running a sex racket and given a severe beating. She says she wasn't sexually assaulted but that everyone, down to the cleaning person, took turns beating her. She was locked up for two days, then released. It was the breaking point for her.

She says, 'At that time, they were giving identity cards to the women who were working on the project. Those who had the card were never arrested. I went to the office and asked for the card and I was told to first go for a health check-up. I went three or four times to the office, and volunteered to do some work, and they gave a card to me.'

Now that she had what she wanted, Mobile Pragya escaped into the field, and for almost two months the programme staff couldn't find her. When they did eventually they assured her they didn't want the card back. Listing out her skills, they told her she should start putting them to use in Ashodaya. They praised the way she presented herself well and her confident manner of speaking. Mobile Pragya in all her life had never received appreciation for anything. She decided to give it a shot and joined Ashodaya as a member of its enabling environment team,[2] which was engaged in crisis response.

Mobile Pragya soon became the lead member of the team. Her job was to go to the court, explain the Ashodaya programme, and secure the release of sex workers who had been arrested. Fearful at first, she finally developed the courage to go to the same police station where she had been beaten for days to negotiate directly with the police. Her status with the police was markedly different when she presented herself as a confident, card-carrying member of Ashodaya.

~

Mobile Pragya says, 'I learnt from the project that to do sex work itself was not a crime. I understood what the law says about how to arrest women. Shinu and I were the ones who started the enabling environment work in Ashodaya.'

At this she nods at Shinu, a kothi sex worker who had been sitting beside Mobile Pragya throughout our discussion. I notice him only now, as I had been focusing on Mobile Pragya. Shinu is just a fraction over five feet, balding, and talks with expansive hand gestures, slicing the air in unpredictable directions, each hand as though with an independent mind of its own, unrelated to its twin on the other side. He has a rather high-pitched voice, a slight lisp, and an altogether endearing manner. He launches into a long description of different incidents where Mobile Pragya and he intervened successfully. After some time, at a sharp glance from her, he senses that he has been going on too long and ends abruptly.

Mobile Pragya continues: 'One day the DCP said, go and talk to the street-level police, train them on the procedures. This DCP had already visited our programme.[3] Once a murder had happened and some sex workers had been picked up. They had been in jail for three months. The inspector came to my house to discuss the situation with me and asked me how we could approach the case.'

Mobile Pragya had started working with and for the police, rather than being their victim. She had earned her Ashodaya card.

~

When the sex workers got cards from the police, it was their own attitude more than anyone else's that changed. It gave them a surge of confidence. They began to fight back, literally.

It began one day when a rowdy was beating his sex worker girlfriend on the street, just outside the Drop-In Centre. This man had also been snatching mangalsutras regularly from sex workers. Some of the sex workers came out and told him to stop, but that only increased the severity of his blows. Soon, a crowd of sex workers had come out of the office, creating a commotion, and suddenly there was a cracking sound – one woman had delivered a hard slap on the goon's cheek. The man stood on the spot stunned, mouth open, dazed and bewildered. Within seconds, all the sex workers were on him, raining blows on him. After thrashing him, three of the women took the goon to the police station, squeezing into an autorickshaw.

Mobile Pragya says, 'This started happening regularly. Always two kothis would first catch hold of the goon, and one was always Shinu. He goes crazy when it comes to beating goons. He often had to be pulled off, for the women to take over. After the beating, we took them to the police station, or first the hospital.' I can't quite picture tiny Shinu beating up dangerous goons and my incredulity must have showed. He smiles shyly, pleased by the recognition he is getting. He says, 'The kothis were having the same problem. The same bad things, being taken by force by the panthi boyfriends. Some of the MSMs got together and formed their own crisis response team.'

The goons then started coming to the Drop-In Centre. They were scared, saying, 'Look, we are not enemies.' The sex workers earmarked one day every month when the goons and boyfriends could come in for coffee and snacks. They would be told about the work the women were doing and that they should feel proud. The sex workers asked the men how they would protect the women. No one told the goons why they had really been invited. The women simply called it a Men's Club, and the men believed it, says Mobile Pragya laughing. Roles had reversed.

~

Initially, the crisis response was spontaneous, with no clear guidelines. Then, with experience, it became more structured. If a woman was in distress, she would pretend she wanted to go to the bathroom and call the crisis response team, and they would arrive on the scene quickly. They started developing safety guidelines such as: 'Don't go to a lodge if you aren't comfortable with the place. If you need to go, take two other friends, take phone numbers. If the client says we are going to one place and takes you to a different place, call a friend or leave a message.' It became the norm that all crises had to be solved within two hours.

The campaign against violence did not erupt overnight. It was like a drumbeat that began slowly – then got louder as the months went by. In the first year, the DCP himself might intervene after some horrific incident; the next week a woman would be assaulted by goons just outside the city. Slowly women stopped being kidnapped in broad daylight from the City Bus Stand, though they would still be grabbed by force at dusk in the bylanes of the city. But a movement had begun and could not be stopped.

Within a year, that is, by 2006, the drive against violence was happening simultaneously across Avahan, with varying levels of success. The most effective sites were those where the response was led by the community of sex workers and involved vigorous advocacy, sharing data with the police, media, and others who could have influence. Women's groups to combat violence were mushrooming in all but the North-Eastern states. The movement to better the day-to-day lives of sex workers, especially by addressing the issue of violence, was a key reason why the numbers of women joining Avahan's local programmes started skyrocketing – or, to use today's phrase, 'went viral'.

18

Taking Wing

Notice

1. *Board member is only sex workers*
2. *She cannot be minor*
3. *She must be ready to go in front of media as a sex worker*
4. *She must answer to the community*
5. *She will leave the position if she is not performing and told to do so*
6. *No clients during working hours*
7. *No alcohol during working hours*

~

By the end of 2005, almost every sex worker in Mysore – by then a total of about 2050 – was enrolled for services with Ashodaya. Of these, twenty-five were working for the programme. Condoms went out, the clinic was running, and the operation against violence was under way. Internally however, it sometimes seemed like chaos. Often it wasn't clear who was supposed to be doing what, and there was too much dependence on a few individuals.

I talked to Shantamma, a sex worker who has been with Ashodaya from its earliest days and seen it grow through all its phases. She is in her forties, and wears a crisp sari, smartly pinned at the shoulder. She speaks precisely in short sentences, always in good humour.

'We were having problems with rowdies, police, all the time. We were always talking a lot of big things in our own community centre, but nobody recognized us on the outside. We started realizing the Ashodaya staff couldn't solve all these problems for us. But what to do by ourselves? This was going through our minds when one day Sushena ma'am challenged us to stand on our own feet – "I'll support from behind. From now on you decide."

'We knew that at Sonagachi sex workers had got recognition from society because they had their own organization. One day we talked among ourselves and said, "We will form our own strong organization." They gave us a table, two chairs, and a cupboard. We called a lawyer and took his advice. He told us what is a board, why we needed that and some committees to do different things. He said the first thing is to decide what rules a person must agree to, if she is to be on the board.'

Deciding the rules proved contentious and took several meetings, each attended by over a hundred sex workers. The lawyer explained to everyone that Ashodaya was being registered as a society, and there would be a five-person board, with rules. He laid out the process: anyone could suggest a rule, and there would be discussion for as long as needed, and then a vote by show of hands.

Shantamma says, 'It wasn't clear who was in charge of these meetings. There was a lot of shouting, and cross-talk. The first point taken up was if only sex workers could serve on the board. It went on for hours, and people almost came to blows.'

The process went on over multiple meetings for two months. Finally, the sex workers agreed on six rules for board members, and these were prominently displayed on the noticeboard at the Drop-In Centre.

~

In September 2005, Ashodaya had its first election. There would be five board positions – president, vice president, secretary, joint secretary and treasurer. Six more positions came from the different talukas of the district. There would also be two MSM positions, which would have their own elections. Any registered sex worker could nominate herself as a candidate for election to one of the five executive committee positions.

Shantamma laughs. 'It went off peacefully, through simple show of hands. This was because there was no contest! Twenty people had initially filed nominations. Of these, thirteen withdrew on election day when they realized that as board members they would be required to go by the strict rules displayed on the noticeboard. The main reason was that people were not willing to publicly say that they were sex workers.

'After the board positions, three working committees were made – for enabling environment, community mobilization, and service delivery. Each had five members, one leader. Community members willing to go by the criteria had to be searched out, one by one. It took weeks.

'These became action committees. For example, if a sex worker had been picked up by the police, she would try to get a call through to one of the enabling environment committee members, who would immediately get into action. When responsibility came to them, the board and committee members realized it was not about them personally, it was for lots of individuals that they were looking after.'

~

Shantamma continues: 'The second election happened three years later, in 2008. Previous office bearers were not allowed to contest. This time it was more formal. There were ballot papers, votes were put into a box, no show of hands.

'After seeing how the first board worked, it looked attractive to many community members. They felt that the board members had status. So there were lots of people who stood for election. Each had her own platform and they were all canvassing in the field. If they knew someone would not vote for them, some of them gave a warning: if you don't vote for me I know how to handle you. They were threatening opponents' supporters not to come on voting day. A few were even going around providing free breakfast and lunch packets.' Shantamma dissolves into laughter as she recalls this.

'Some who contested didn't get a single vote – even their own. One of the winners blew her savings on five thousand rupees of firecrackers. Those who lost threw away the flowers they had brought thinking they would win, and went back very angry. Afterwards they became disruptive. Some who lost had good skills, and we solved the problem by putting them on one of the committees. Then they were happy and did good work.'

In the beginning there were no performance rules, but the committees slowly formed the rules. Every fifteen days the committee members got feedback, because the president would go to the field and talk to sex workers there. The board people also got feedback: Mary, the president, was removed for drinking and not doing work, and so was Kavita, the treasurer. The committee members also got feedback from the community from a box where anyone could drop their complaints. The box was opened every fifteen days.

~

On 1 December 2008, World AIDS Day, the deputy commissioner of police inaugurated a novel eatery in Mysore, at a prime location right next to the Mysore Palace. It was unique because it was managed entirely by twelve sex workers, male and female, many of them HIV positive. It was the eponymous Ashodaya Restaurant.

The restaurant was an attempt by the sex worker community to launch a business that would enable them to become self-sufficient. They were becoming increasingly aware that their organization was dependent on outside funding and that the funding from Avahan would end in a few years. They also relied on Sushena to raise funds and decided that generating their own steady source of income was essential. Sushena warned them of the difficulties, told them that the project would pay the rent, but the rest of it – finding space, setting up the eatery, managing it day to day – would be entirely up to them.

Many sex workers turned out to be good cooks and it was not difficult to staff the kitchen. The menu was simple, consisting mainly of breakfast snacks such as dosa, pongal, and idli. Hot poori-bhaji was always available.

It all went well for a while. Local and even mainstream media in the state covered the novelty of a sex workers' restaurant. The Ashodaya Restaurant had a steady stream of customers – mainly the sex workers' boyfriends and their panthis. Occasionally the odd foreign tourist would come in out of curiosity. But slowly, the footfalls began to decline. It became obvious that the public was not ready to receive food from the hands of a sex worker, and that too someone who might be HIV positive. This problem might well have been anticipated, but the community hadn't seen it coming.

Ashodaya Restaurant ran for almost two years, in which it never covered its operating costs. Then the inevitable happened – it folded.

～

Today, Ashodaya is being managed day to day by six people working collectively, reporting again to a board of community members, as it has been since 2005. There are three community members – Shahid, Shantamma, and Kavita – and three staff – KT, Venu, and Syed. All of them have been with Ashodaya since the early years. Each person has a specific area of focus – for example, grant proposals, individual donor programmes, organization running, and the Ashodaya Academy (of which more soon). They support each other, and many decisions are collectively made. More surprising, there has never been a designated head of Ashodaya. I ask Sushena, 'Organizations rarely last as a collective. Were you always in charge behind the scenes?'

'Nothing happened overnight,' she says. 'It was a sliding scale. There was me, the staff, and the community of sex workers. From 2005, after the elections, I began to let go slowly. I was focusing on making concepts clear, took the lead in strategy, fundraising, led all technical things. Always, the idea was to get the community to learn new things. They got trained to share knowledge – through video, PowerPoint, storytelling. They started contributing to research papers that serious academics were working on. They became such good orators. They started documenting crises, making savings, doing outreach work. The mistake we make is in assuming people can perform only up to a certain level.'

I ask about the six-member leadership team, and how they function today without one person as leader. 'Each person has a certain role, and someone else acts like a shadow. For example, Shahid oversees Ashodaya Academy – our global learning site – and Syed is his shadow; KT manages all programmes on the ground. They have big titles, which are good to present to the external world. There may be squabbles, but it has worked out very well, all these years. The key is to have clear values and realize that values are meaningful only in action.'

From 2014 Sushena had begun to feel she could withdraw entirely from Ashodaya and describes her role today as minimal. She has worked very hard to ensure she becomes dispensable.

∼

In early 2004, an utterly destitute sex worker was picked up by the Ashodaya programme staff from the streets of Mysore. Five years later she was in Colombo, making a presentation to an audience of over five hundred, at the International AIDS conference. That same year she was invited to join UNAIDS' twenty-seven-member Programme Coordinating Board (PCB). She presented her views to the head of UNAIDS and the entire PCB on how HIV prevention programmes in different parts of the world could be strengthened, speaking from her personal experience as an HIV positive practising sex worker.

She is Kavita, the sex worker from Shimoga whose story we heard earlier. Kavita spoke to me about her unlikely journey, from barely surviving on the streets of Mysore when she joined Ashodaya to globally respected expert in HIV prevention delivery.

'Around 2006, Ashodaya had started to do a lot of training.[1] I went as trainer to many places such as Tamil Nadu, Maharashtra, and Sonagachi in Kolkata. I saw that sex workers' problems are the same everywhere. When I met sex workers in other parts of India I said, "At Ashodaya we sex workers are developing solutions to problems, nobody is doing it for us." This is the main learning I tried to take to other programmes – that you can solve your own problems.

'There was some meeting in Delhi with foreign agencies, and they heard me and other sex workers from Ashodaya speaking. After that I started being invited to foreign countries as part of Ashodaya. I have gone to many different places as a trainer or to speak. Busan which is in Korea, Bangkok, Bali, Belgium, Mexico, Amsterdam. Then Melbourne in Australia, South Africa – Durban – Mozambique, Kenya.

'I found that in foreign countries also, the problems are similar for almost all sex workers. In India it is the boyfriend. In Indonesia and those parts it's all controlled by pimps and the "mummies". In Africa it's drugs. Police, rowdies, and boyfriend issues are common everywhere.

'In Africa every time we visit, the community gets excited and says we want to be like Ashodaya, but after we leave there is no support for them.'

Kavita laughs as she adds, 'When I land in a foreign country, I immediately want to go back home. The places are nice, but often too cold. I can't eat the food. I stick to rice and carry some masala to sprinkle.'

It strikes me that the warmth of Ashodaya, and practising the world's oldest profession on her own terms, off the mean streets of Mysore, is a more congenial place for Kavita than the shores of Lake Geneva. Everything is relative.

~

It was happening not only in Ashodaya. In hundreds of our programme locations across India, sex workers were delivering services, fighting violence, building their own community-based organizations. My team ensured that best practices were continuously being transferred across our sites. Those days, without the benefits of WhatsApp or even the Internet, we relied on face-to-face transfer of knowledge. We convened meetings of all our lead implementing partners in each state once every quarter. Progress was reviewed and learnings shared. After such meetings it became natural for community members to travel to other locations to share and to learn.

Ashodaya stood out in this vast Avahan knowledge exchange network. In 2009 invitations had started coming in from other countries. Sushena asked if Avahan would fund an initiative to convert Ashodaya into a global learning site. The idea was to transfer Ashodaya's learnings through rigorous documentation, dissemination, and training. It was an audacious goal, but I felt it was well worth placing a bet on. Thus began an exciting new chapter in the story of Avahan – the creation of the Ashodaya Academy.

So far, sex workers from more than twenty countries as far flung as Myanmar, Cambodia, China, Vietnam, the Philippines, Papua New Guinea, Indonesia, Kenya, South Africa, and Afghanistan have come to learn at the Ashodaya Academy. Teams from Ashodaya have travelled to many of these countries to build the capacity of sex workers in those nations to manage their own problems as a community. In 2009–10 UNAIDS held training for twelve countries, including Afghanistan and Pakistan, at Ashodaya.

From 2016 to 2018 Ashodaya conducted a seminal community trial of PREP (pre-exposure prophylaxis, when the sex worker's client takes a precautionary ART pill before sex), funded by the Gates Foundation, to investigate whether this intervention would be effective in India. It had to be led by sex workers capable of working with great precision and mutual trust. The results are cited worldwide.

The audacious idea had become a vibrant reality.

Lesedi is a street sex worker in Durban, South Africa, who works with Life Line, an NGO that has been doing exemplary work for more than forty years on issues of emotional wellness of marginalized groups, especially women and youth. Lesedi talked to me about her association with Ashodaya since 2013.

'When I first went to Mysore, what most struck me was that sex workers have the same issues there as here. For example, the biggest problem we faced was the same as in Mysore – violence from the police. We had the attitude "police are our enemies", which was not solving the problem. When we saw how Ashodaya had developed a programme of engaging with the police, it had a very strong impact on us. We came back and did the same thing. We spoke to the police captain and invited them to come and see the risk reduction workshops that we were doing every month. Over time, our relationship with the police changed.

'Ashodaya inspired us. We came back and made our own Drop-In Centre. When we saw the Ashodaya clinic it made us believe we too could do the same. We created our own clinic with a full-time sister [nurse] and part-time doctor. The clinic managed ART and made a big difference.

'Some things are different. Sex workers in Mysore dress modestly in saris, we show a lot of flesh! We have a much bigger problem of alcohol and drugs. Other things are similar – we both have sex work in brothels, taverns, streets, houses, and bushes. Our language and customs are different, but we connect with each other very easily.'

Sushena smiles and agrees: 'An immediate bonding happens between sex workers, no matter where they come from. They connect as a sisterhood.'

~

I spoke to Rethabile, Bokamoso, and Paul, from the excellent NGO HOYMAS in Nairobi. They say they began to develop a belief in themselves after they first visited Ashodaya. They describe Ashodaya's help in building their capacity in outreach methods, setting up and managing a care home, community clinics, and a technical support unit to work with government as Avahan had done with NACO.

The HOYMAS team talks of a two-way 'knowledge transfer' that is happening continuously: 'The Sex Worker Academy Africa (SWAA) was a major initiative inspired by the Ashodaya Academy, and sex workers from Mysore came as trainers to help us set it up. It is a programme for community empowerment and capacity-building, led by and for sex workers. It brings national teams of sex workers from across Africa to develop organizing skills, learn best practices, stimulate national sex worker movements, and strengthen the regional network.'

~

It seems like only yesterday when I first visited Mysore, and discovered the city within, hidden in the shadows, the one being quietly wasted by HIV. It was a bleak site for HIV prevention. But today Ashodaya is a proud global learning site for community-led HIV prevention.

Sex workers like Kavita, Shahid, Mobile Pragya, Neelamma, and others staggered, or were carried in, from the streets, sometimes barely alive. They are now leaders of Ashodaya, respected well beyond Mysore.

It has been an incredible journey.

19

Handing Over

Avahan was set up in April 2003, and by the middle of 2004 our programmes were all running. By the end of 2006, we had become the world's largest-ever privately sponsored HIV prevention programme.

Throughout this narrative, I have emphasized that communities were at the centre of our programme. But they could not have done what they did without training and support – both technical and managerial – from the NGOs we had given grants to. (We called them partners, and they are listed in the appendix.)

What happened in Ashodaya was happening at the same time in hundreds of sites across Avahan, with varying degrees of success. Our partners were building their own programmes across six states. Each was responsible for a whole state, sometimes half of it. Theirs was the challenge of building and operating a programme of a mammoth scale, with the same pan-Avahan strategy of focus on highly at-risk groups, community involvement, and advocacy. They had to do this with quality, and speed, and many partners did that; some fell short, and needed more support, as we will see soon.

By 2009 so much toil by so many people had started bearing fruit. The mood in meetings across our states with groups of sex workers was upbeat. Only a few hands would go up when I asked if anyone

Avahan programme sites (2006)

6 states, 83 districts, 672 towns

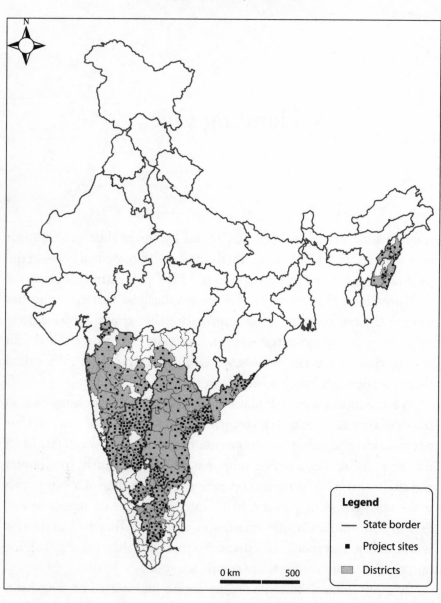

Legend

— State border

▪ Project sites

▭ Districts

0 km   500

had faced violence recently. Nearly all hands shot up when I asked if anyone had a ration card. Life was still tough for a sex worker, but there was a positivity in the air, so different from the early days when despair was the prevalent mood.

~

Avahan began with a goal that was as vague as it was grand – to stem the spread of HIV in India. Just a year into our work we had realized that was impossible, such was the scope and complexity of the epidemic. The foundation had no intention of becoming a perpetual funder of programmes to control India's HIV epidemic, but we wanted to see the job through. So a second goal was created, after discussions with NACO: to create a model of HIV prevention that could be transferred to government. This became the second phase of Avahan, to run from 2008 to 2013. The idea was to transfer by the end of that period all our interventions to government, and they would then on be nurtured by the national programme.

By 2009 we started thinking about the modalities of this transfer of Avahan to the national programme. The process would have to begin soon. Increasingly, it bothered me that we would shut shop and go away when the HIV virus was in retreat and victory proclaimed, leaving the communities vulnerable. Would these groups be nurtured in the same way under government? The thought kept coming back – what will happen to the people who fought the battle at the front line?

~

In the first phase of Avahan, after the rocky welcome from NACO described in chapter 2, we kept our heads down, spending our time mostly in the field. We understood that it was only after we had got dirt under our fingernails that we would be able to speak with authority.

I worked with seven heads of NACO during the ten years I spent with Avahan. The one who stood out was Sujatha Rao – dynamic, approachable, and big-hearted. She headed NACO for a little over three years from 2006 to 2009, a crucial period because a new phase of the national AIDS programme was to be launched in 2007. Sujatha's singular achievement was in ensuring that it was well designed and, for the first time, adequately resourced.

The new national plan, known as NACP3 (National AIDS Control Plan 3), was to run from 2007 to 2012.[1] (The background to these plans has been touched upon in chapter 9.) The development of guidelines and budgets would happen, as was the practice, with inputs from the UN agencies and implementing NGOs. It was a tedious task, but we saw the opportunity to ensure our learnings were absorbed into the national plan. We volunteered to work on nearly every component of the new plan.

Sujatha's staff was limited and mostly not up to the task, and she welcomed our stepping forward. Aparajita Ramakrishnan from our team moved into NACO and put together a team. Working long hours, we managed in less than six months to get everything we had learnt in Avahan and that we considered essential in HIV prevention incorporated into the national plan. The most significant of these was substantial provisions to reduce the vulnerability of sex worker communities. There were steps to ensure their access to government health facilities, ration cards, and safety, among others. When it was all costed out, India's budget for HIV went up by five times.

It was a milestone in our process of transition, and we felt good about having played a shaping role in the new national HIV/AIDS plan. The methods had been transferred; now the physical transfer of the programme remained.

~

By 2009 the trends in decline of the HIV epidemic in India were encouraging. In state after state new cases of HIV were coming down steadily. We were also almost two years into the transition phase of Avahan. With three years left in our grant, we spoke to Sujatha Rao about moving the eighty-three districts where we were running HIV prevention programmes over to the national programme. NACO didn't have the budget to immediately take over our funding, nor the capacity to oversee the absorption of the new districts. We agreed that the transfer would be done in three tranches: 10 per cent of our districts in 2010, 20 per cent in 2011, and the balance 70 per cent in 2012. Our nine strongest districts would be transferred in the first tranche. The only Avahan district we left out of the entire transfer was the Ashodaya programme in Mysore.

We explained the plans for transfer to the government system to sex worker communities across our programme sites. We used the analogy of a child having grown up, now ready to step out on her own. There was some grumbling and a few angry accusations, but in most of our sites sex workers took the announcement in their stride. It was good to see how far they had come in terms of standing confidently on their own feet.

All seemed good till the second tranche was transferred in 2011, but the third and last tranche, in 2012, was to pose fresh challenges.

~

Nellore is a coastal town in Andhra Pradesh with a population of a little over five lakh, located 175 kilometres due north of Chennai. I had left Chennai for Nellore by car at six in the morning and was feeling drained by the heat and humidity as we drove in.

This was in April 2012, five years since I had last visited. At that time, our programme in Nellore had been struggling. My diary from that visit in 2007 says: 'The NGO had with difficulty scraped together some ten destitute women who had been practising [sex work] on the street. The air was one of utter hopelessness.' The women were from the villages around Nellore, travelling up and down every day, first to sell their meagre produce and after that their bodies, probably for less than the price of a few cabbages. They were dishevelled and grimy, in rags that barely covered their skeletal frames. They stared into the distance and would not answer a single question I asked. The meeting was short, and I remember how disturbed I felt.

This time, I was joined in Nellore by Matangi Jayaram, my colleague who managed our programme in Nellore which had been transitioned to NACO in our second tranche in 2011. This meant that it had made huge progress in five years, to rank among the top 30 per cent of Avahan's programmes, and I found that astounding, considering where it had been five years ago.

The community centre – a much bigger and brighter place than the one I had seen last time – was packed with more than forty female sex workers, as well as a few MSMs and transgender people. Several women had dressed up for what they were treating as a special occasion. We entered into a freewheeling discussion. I learnt that there were hardly any incidents of violence against sex workers in Nellore. The police chief, a short, portly man with a pencil moustache, had appeared, and self-effacingly told me he had done nothing – the orders had come 'from high above' (which meant the political leadership).

Nearly all the sex workers had mobile phones and ration cards. Almost everyone had a savings account – though few had any savings in it. Governance processes among the sex worker communities were in place. As I examined the registers I saw that record-keeping was systematic. Their relationship with the State AIDS Control Society – the local arm of NACO – was strong, with plenty of support from the government system. Access to the full range of government services made a big difference. Some of the women even said that life was better after transition, and that truly warmed my heart. One even said her rates had gone up after the transfer!

I said, deliberately aiming to provoke, 'What you all are doing here is wonderful. But do you realize we can't fund this programme forever? What will you do if this centre has to be closed?' Even though programmes like those in Nellore had been transferred, we had decided to continue supporting districts on the community vulnerability front till the end of phase two. Hence my question on whether the community could pay the rent and run the community centre on their own.

The general response was 'We'll manage ourselves', accompanied by clapping and laughter. There were also some worried faces.

With more questioning, one sex worker, who seemed to be expressing the sentiment in the room, said, 'We need support from Avahan for some more time, till we stand on our feet.' Many of the local NGOs who had been in charge said the same thing. They were referring to support in running the programme, rather than pure financial support, which would now come from government.

~

I was also seeing many programmes that were more adept at providing outreach services but were struggling with aspects such as working with the police or government to secure their rights. In 2012, when our last sixty-seven districts were to be handed over, and the final phase of Avahan had less than a year to run, it became clear that these communities would be left vulnerable and needed more support.

We therefore decided to fund a much smaller phase three of Avahan, which would run for another three years, from 2014 to 2017. The idea was to nurture and strengthen the weaker sex worker communities to a point where they could manage vulnerability reduction activities on their own, through their own community-based organizations. We agreed with NACO that while the service delivery portion of the erstwhile Avahan districts would be funded by government, most of the community activities would be funded by Avahan for another three years. Two Avahan staff, Matangi Jayaram and Sameer Kumta, stayed on to manage phase three.

The third phase of the Avahan grant was awarded to Swasthi, a Bangalore-based NGO. Their mandate was to work in forty-five of the eighty-three Avahan districts that had been transferred to government, but still required support on the community front, based on a detailed independent survey. Swasthi began working directly with eighty-four community-based organizations in these forty-five districts that together reached a population of over 1.3 lakh female and male sex workers and transgender persons. It was a period of intense work for Swasthi. They measured impact carefully, defining levels of vulnerability of a community-based organization along a five-point scale that rated different aspects of its ability to fight violence and access entitlements. They worked with each community-based organization to strengthen governance and management processes and build essential skills. They did a tough job splendidly.

The results speak for themselves. Over the course of this third phase, in these forty-five districts, incidents of violence came down from 23 per cent to 16 per cent, and 87 per cent of sex workers had acquired bank accounts, as compared to 50 per cent at the start. Through these and other activities, consistent condom use went from 72 per cent to 90 per cent and STI prevalence came down from 13 per cent to 8 per cent. By 2017, it was estimated that 93 per cent of sex workers were able to manage their own vulnerability factors.[2]

~

Commercial sex work will never be an entirely safe occupation. Sex workers still must fight to get access to government amenities to which they are entitled. But it can be said that Avahan through all its phases made a strong contribution. Most importantly, we stayed the course.

Epilogue

The defeat of HIV is one of India's great public health achievements. Avahan joined the war against HIV in 2003 when the epidemic was at its zenith. An estimated 4.8 million people were then living with HIV (later revised to 2.6 million). Today that figure is 2.1 million. The prevalence of HIV in India is 0.22 per cent, which is less than that in the United States. An estimated 150,000 people were getting infected by HIV in 2003 – today it is 88,000.[1] In 2015, HIV was one of only two health conditions where India had met the UN's Millennium Development Goals.

However, the containment of HIV in India is likely to always stay one of India's least celebrated public health victories. This speaks of the high levels of apathy that still surround this most stigmatized of health conditions. Thousands of people, most of them brave female sex workers, fought at the front line of the war against HIV, driven by a huge sense of community, giving it their all. It is a pity that their selfless contributions will never be recognized because of sheer stigma.

HIV is a cunning foe, and several national programmes have paid the price for declaring victory over it prematurely. The best that can be said in HIV prevention is 'so far so good', and constant vigilance is required to prevent the virus from striking again. The worry today

comes from HIV arising from injecting drug use. The North-East
continues to cause concern in this context. In Manipur, HIV prevalence
is the highest in India, at 1.2 per cent; Mizoram and Nagaland have
the next highest prevalence among Indian states, close to 1 per cent. In
Punjab because of uncontained injecting drug use, new HIV infections
are rising. The biggest change has been the advent of ART, and its
provision through the national HIV programme. Because of ART,
HIV is no longer a death sentence and a person who has acquired the
virus can plan to live a long and productive life.

~

In 2004, India had seventy-eight districts that had an HIV prevalence
of 1 per cent or more. All but one of these districts were taken up
by Avahan, and they all fell in the six states in which we worked
from 2003 onward. These states were Manipur and Nagaland, and
the much larger, contiguous states of Maharashtra, Tamil Nadu,
Andhra Pradesh, and Karnataka. By 2006, Avahan was providing
HIV prevention services to over 270,000 members of high-risk
groups, mainly female sex workers. Each person's record was
being tracked individually. At the height of Avahan, we were
delivering services in eighty-three districts, and 672 towns within
these districts. At that point we were distributing a little over thirteen
million condoms[2] a month. (I like to think that if you put a year's
supply of these condoms end to end they would suffice to go around
the earth!)

The speed at which Avahan moved is also amazing – we had
established ourselves well within three years as the world's largest-
ever privately sponsored HIV prevention programme. *Lancet* in 2013
estimated that in the period 2003–13, Avahan averted over 600,000
HIV infections. In 2015 Avahan was one of eighteen global public
health programmes recognized in the prestigious 'Millions Saved'
list of the Centre for Global Development. It is today considered one

of the most well-documented public health programmes, with over three hundred peer-reviewed journal articles, scores of monographs and media features, two Harvard Business School Case Studies, and significant mentions in over thirty books.

Avahan was driven by an almost obsessive emphasis on scale. There is nothing complicated as such about the elements of HIV prevention – ensuring condom usage, managing STIs, creating awareness. And yet, there had never been an example of HIV delivery at very large scale prior to Avahan. In India this was because there were many complex barriers that came in the way, primary among which were the absence of data and communities of high-risk groups that had no power.

Avahan developed a model of working at scale by addressing these barriers systematically. Not only did Avahan build the model, but we successfully transferred that running model to government. I am proud that we worked hard to erase the name Avahan forever from the programmes we had run, as we transferred them into the national programme. That too is a rarity in public health.

What has all this meant for the lives of sex workers? Sex work will always be a tough profession. But today (and Swasthi's figures are some indication) the vulnerability of sex workers to violence has decreased and their ability to access health services is much greater.

The profession itself has changed with the advent of the mobile phone and social media – many sex workers today even have Facebook accounts. These developments have almost eliminated the middleman and lessened the need for the woman to walk the streets to get clients. Again, it has made the profession that much safer.

Our overall goal was to make a strong contribution towards stemming the growth of HIV in India. It was also our goal to enable dissemination of that model more broadly through adequate documentation. It is safe to say we met those goals in full measure.

I mention all these things not to sound our own trumpet but to acknowledge the selfless work put in by thousands of the people most vulnerable to the virus. It is their victory. It calls for recognition long overdue.

~

I joined Avahan as a person who thought he knew a lot, but I discovered that I was looking at life really from a very limited vantage point. Travelling to far-flung places, meeting people who lived in the most desperate of circumstances, I was exposed to an India that shocked and touched me profoundly. It brought me face-to-face with truths far stranger than fiction.

I was both humbled and inspired by the courage and selflessness of the communities that I got to know at close quarters. Today when times get rough I think of any one of the sex workers I came to know more closely through the programme, who face up to much greater adversities with courage, and I draw strength from that. Avahan was grace, a life experience that changed me forever.

Walking away from Avahan, having transferred the programme to its natural owner NACO, gave me immense personal satisfaction. As the years went by, I have got busy with other things. But from time to time, my thoughts do go back to the times we spent in those strangest of places, with the most unusual of people.

I will always think of myself as part of that larger community. But would that community still remember and accept me? I inadvertently got a chance to find out, a couple of years ago. I was in Pune, and my flight back to Delhi was delayed. On a whim, I asked the driver to take me to Budhwar Peth, telling him I'd be back in no more than an hour. He nodded, after giving me a sharp look of disapproval in the mirror. I can imagine what he was thinking.

After a quick call to the NGO who worked in one of the sections of the brothel, I was soon climbing up the kind of creaky stairs that I had navigated many times before. I could feel my heart beating as I climbed each step, not knowing what to expect. It was a joy to be fussed over by the many sex workers there, who remembered me well, and to see how much things had improved for them. They insisted that I get a manicure and head massage at the beauty parlour they had started. I demurred, saying I had a flight to catch, but still went back to the car smelling of perfume. The driver frowned and imperceptibly shook his head.

I visited Swasthi's office in Bangalore for this book, and interviewed two female sex workers I had known from before – Marie and Hema. They welcomed me like a long-lost friend and we relived some old times, poring over their photo library, especially their images of Bill's visit to their office to meet the sex workers. Both Marie and Hema were dressed in wonderful saris and had their best jewellery on. It dawned on me as I drove away that they had dressed up in their very best just to welcome me, and I was touched.

For this book, I've had to travel back to several erstwhile Avahan locales and reconnect with friends from the community again. Our worlds will always be different, but we haven't forgotten our times together. I am proud to say today that I am beloved of sex workers all over India, in a way that no man could ever hope to be. That, I think, is an achievement!

In 2013, I was a senior fellow at the Harvard School of Public Health. I taught a course I designed called 'Scaling up public health delivery – lessons in leadership' that was based on Avahan. I learnt a lot from this experience of trying to put all our learnings from Avahan into frameworks that could be taught in a classroom.

Easily the best class in my course was when I managed, with great difficulty, to hook up my students in Cambridge, Massachusetts, with twenty sex workers, assembled at our intervention site in Mysore, Karnataka. It was a fascinating reversal of roles, with the least educated offering life lessons to the intellectual elite. At one point, one of my students asked of the group in Mysore, 'What is leadership?' The answer, from one of the sex workers was immediate: 'Leadership is serving your community.'

Like a proud father, I just stood aside and watched, smiling.

~

Early into Avahan, as we began to scale up, it occurred to me that the principles we were using were so fundamental – surely, they must be universal? Can scaling up also be achieved in other areas of public health delivery through a combination of data use by front-line workers, active involvement of communities, and smart advocacy? I wanted, after Avahan, to test that idea out in another sphere of public health delivery. Today, I'm testing out that dream – applying the principles of scaling up that we learnt from Avahan to maternal and child health, working in thousands of the remotest villages of Rajasthan. I do that through my start-up non-profit – the Antara Foundation. With Avahan, I was a huge funder of a programme deploying over 150 grass-roots NGOs; today, I am one of those grass-roots NGOs, perennially looking for funding. It's character-building, for sure.

It's been four years now, enough to assert that indeed those lessons from Avahan are universal. It's been a great adventure so far – but wait, that's another story.

Appendix

Background Facts about HIV/Aids

- Overview of the global HIV epidemic
- India's national HIV programme
- HIV prevention strategies
- Structure of the Avahan programme

Global HIV epidemic

The first official recognition of the HIV virus came in 1981 when the Centres for Disease Control in Atlanta recognized a new disease, characterized by a progressive failure of the body's immune system. As the HIV infection progressed within the victim's system, he would enter finally into the stage of AIDS, when any simple infection could prove fatal. Before the advent of treatment, this amounted to a slow, agonizing death, where the victim lost most of his weight and control over bodily functions.

It was soon established that the virus was spread by the exchange of blood or semen – through unprotected sex, sharing of needles, exposure to infected blood, and from mother to unborn baby. In 1983 Robert Gallo in the United States and Luc Montagnier in France shared the Nobel Prize when they separately isolated the HIV virus and established it as the root cause.

The dramatic emergence of HIV in the United States, with the first cases detected in the early 1980s, brought global attention to the virus. By the mid-1980s, HIV cases in the United States were appearing primarily on the West and East Coasts, and at first it was thought to be a disease that was primarily being spread through sex between gay men. The disease came with huge levels of stigma, with victims ostracized, thrown out in the streets by landlords, even refused treatment by hospitals. By the late 1990s, with greater awareness, and the advent of treatment, the epidemic in America had been contained.

The battlegrounds against HIV were now in Africa and, increasingly, Asia. HIV epidemics in Africa and in Asia are different. African countries have what are known as 'generalized epidemics', whereas Asian countries have 'concentrated epidemics'. The WHO defines an HIV epidemic as generalized when the virus has infected more than 2 per cent of the adult population. When we started Avahan in 2003, adult HIV prevalence in South Africa was 28.9 per cent, and in Botswana it was 37.3 per cent.[1] Multi-partner sexual relationships and a high level of unprotected sex were the reasons why the virus had spread into the general population in many African countries.

WHO defines a concentrated epidemic as one where HIV has infected less than 2 per cent of the adult general population, and over 5 per cent of defined high-risk groups. These groups are female sex workers; men who have sex with men, including male sex workers; regular clients of sex workers, especially truckers; transgender people; and injecting drug users. Asian countries such as Thailand and Cambodia had concentrated epidemics. In 2002 in Cambodia, adult HIV prevalence was 2.6 per cent but as high as 28.8 per cent among female sex workers. As early as 1994 those figures were 1.6 per cent and 19 per cent respectively in Thailand.[2]

India's HIV epidemic

In the early years of the new millennium, India had a worrying concentrated epidemic. According to NACO, national HIV prevalence was estimated at 0.8 per cent (translating to an estimate of 4.8 million people infected) and climbing. Prevalence among sex workers was over 5 per cent. HIV prevalence had crossed 2 per cent in more than twenty-five districts by 2005. The sheer size of India was what was causing such grave concern globally. A single district in India with a population of over two million could be compared in size with many African countries.

NACO is the apex body that sets the framework (methods, costing norms) within which HIV prevention and treatment programmes are managed. This is developed in consultation with the World Bank, UNAIDS, implementing NGOs, Indian and global experts, and other stakeholders. It is formalized into a National AIDS Control Plan that is announced every five years. Avahan spanned two national plans, NACP2 (1999–2006) and NACP3 (2007–12.) NACO works through State AIDS Control Societies. They directly fund NGOs that implement programmes with different risk groups in their respective states.

It was only in 2003 that the US Food and Drug Administration approved the first rapid test for HIV. In India, ART started to become available only in 2010. Absence of treatment discouraged people living with HIV from coming forward for testing, and they were reluctant to participate in prevention programmes.

Measuring HIV levels, and treatment

There are two measures of HIV infection in an individual: CD4 and viral load counts. Both are blood tests available free through the Indian government system.

The usual measures of HIV in a population are prevalence and incidence numbers or percentages. HIV is treated using a regimen of ART drugs. (See also endnotes for the epilogue.)

1. **CD4 count** is the number of CD4 cells per cubic millilitre of blood, which is a measure of the body's immunity. HIV positive persons with a CD4 count above 500 are in good health. The HIV virus attacks the 'T-Cells' in the blood stream. These cells in turn manage the white blood cells that defend the body from infection.
2. **Viral load** is the measure of HIV virus levels in the blood. The number of HIV particles in a millilitre of blood is a measure of the progression of HIV in the body.
3. **Prevalence** is the measure of the percentage of people infected with the HIV virus in a given population. Blood samples are taken (without taking donor's name) and tested for HIV. The sample is often taken by government from the population of women attending government antenatal care clinics, where HIV testing is mandatory.
4. **Incidence** is the number of new infections that occur every year in a given population. This is difficult to estimate – it is possible to say a person is infected, but not when he or she got infected. One rough measure used in HIV programmes is prevalence in the under-24-years age group, because sex workers would first get infected when they enter into sex work at an early age.
5. **Antiretroviral treatment** is a cocktail of drugs that is used to manage HIV levels in an infected person. It is necessary to maintain a strict regimen when taking ART to prevent the body developing resistance.

Prevention strategies

The goal of HIV prevention programmes in concentrated epidemics is to reduce HIV in high-risk groups and thereby prevent a spillover into the general population. HIV prevention programmes follow three strategies to achieve this goal.

The first is ensuring that condom usage is consistently high (over 70 per cent) in high-risk groups. The second is ensuring that ulcerative STIs such as syphilis, which fuel HIV transmission, are contained. The third is behaviour-changing communications.

Deploying these strategies requires data on the number of people in each high-risk group, categorized by the level of risky behaviour such as the number of clients per day and extent of condom usage. This estimation can only be done by directly involving members of the risk groups in the process. It is intimate information that sex workers don't easily share outside their own community.

Avahan programme structure

Avahan was launched by the Bill & Melinda Gates Foundation in 2003 with an initial commitment of $200 million (2003–08). There was a second phase of Avahan (2008–13) and the combined spending over ten years was $375 million. (The third phase of Avahan required only a small incremental increase.) These funds were deployed through a pyramid structure, deploying almost ten thousand people, operating at five levels:

1. Avahan core team (16): Foundation staff based out of cities in four states (Mumbai, Bangalore, Chennai, Hyderabad) and in Delhi, with backgrounds in private sector and in public health (e.g., specialists in infectious diseases, communications, advocacy, monitoring, and evaluation). Typically, each state had one Avahan staff member responsible for managing the main implementing partners for that state. Other Avahan staff managed specific cross-cutting functions (e.g., communications and advocacy). Many of these staff were under thirty-five years, and for all it was their first major managerial job.

2. (A) State lead partners (SLPs or Partners): Seven large international (5) and domestic (2) NGOs chosen to implement the Avahan programme in all or part of a single state. They were:
   - Maharashtra: Family Health International (Washington, DC); Pathfinder International (Boston)
   - Andhra Pradesh: International HIV-AIDS Alliance (Bristol, UK); Hindustan Latex PPT (Hyderabad)
   - Tamil Nadu: Voluntary Health Services (Chennai)

- Karnataka: University of Winnipeg, Canada-ICHAP Programme
- Manipur and Nagaland: Emmanuel Hospitals Association, and University of Melbourne.
- Truckers Programme – Transport Corporation of India Foundation

(B) Cross-cutting Implementing Partners (IPs): International and domestic NGOs and agencies chosen to implement the Avahan programme for cross-cutting functions supporting all the state programmes. There were eight in all, of whom three were Indian:

- Advocacy and communications: PATH, Seattle
- Monitoring and evaluation: Family Health International; Johns Hopkins University; University of Laval; University of Toronto; London School of Hygiene and Tropical Medicine; Indian Council for Medical Research (Government of India)

3. Implementing NGOs (over 150): Agencies selected by SLPs to implement the Avahan programme in local areas (e.g., districts) within each state.

4. Front-line workers (about 8500): Employed by each implementing NGO to deliver services to communities within their local areas. There were two types: peer workers – high-risk group members who worked part-time for the NGO and delivered services individually to an assigned portfolio of outside community members (40–60 per peer); outreach workers – typically non-community members who provided management and technical support to the peer workers (typically one outreach worker for ten peers).

Notes

Prologue

1   Andhra Pradesh was bifurcated into two states, Andhra Pradesh and Telangana, in 2014. I will use the name Andhra Pradesh throughout the book, to refer to the unified state that existed when we were working.

1. First Night Out

1   Today, this is NH6. The numbering of several national highways has changed over the years. Throughout, I use the numbering that prevailed when we worked on Avahan.

2   This was NACO's estimate at that time. In 2006, a revised figure of 2.6 million was accepted after a change in the estimation methodology.

3   As distinct from peer workers who do the same thing but are from the sex worker community themselves.

4   Of course, there were also Muslim sex workers. However, the black burkha is also a perfect disguise, protecting the wearer from harassment by police and goons. Therefore, sex workers of all faiths, including men, occasionally donned these outfits.

2. Taking the Plunge

1   Increased to $200 million six months later.

2   This was by no means an original thought. I didn't know enough then to get into details, but I had been reading about a few programmes in HIV prevention

that were focused on the sex worker – Thailand's national programme, the Sonagachi project in Kolkata, and USAID's own programme APAC in Tamil Nadu. The foundation must have felt reaching sex workers would be an almost impossible task.

3   Today, the foundation's offices in Seattle are two elegant, soaring glass structures located close to the iconic Seattle Needle.

4   There was substance to the minister's statement. A September 2012 US National Intelligence Council report, *The Next Wave of HIV/AIDS: Nigeria, Ethiopia, Russia, India, and China*, had forecast that India could have 20 to 25 million cases of HIV-AIDS by 2010.

5   'India Rebuffs Bill Gates in Aids Row', *Guardian* (London), 11 November 2002; 'Bill Gates Has Overdone It', *Times of India* (19 November 2002) headline quoting Human Resources Minister M.M. Joshi.

6   I was on McKinsey's rolls till 1 April 2003, transitioning my client responsibilities while also working on Avahan. This eased my moving out, and it was a nice gesture by the Firm.

7   UNAIDS/WHO, *Epidemiological Fact Sheet on HIV/AIDS and Sexually Transmitted Infections – 2004 Update*.

3. Into the Shadowlands

1   The women of the Kalavanthula caste were traditional courtesans who used to be patronized by the royal family of the region. As those empires crumbled, the women were left in their grand homes to fend for themselves. When we visited, there were a few hundred Kalavanthulas still living in bungalows that were going to seed, in and around the town of Peddapuram in coastal Andhra Pradesh. They did not like to be considered ordinary sex workers but saw themselves as inheritors of a grand tradition of gracious living, music, and dance. We visited a few in their homes – they were genteel, some were beautiful, and they were all clearly struggling, neither here nor there in a uniquely sad way.

2   J. Vandepitte, et al., 'Estimates of the Number of Female Sex Workers in Different Regions of the World', April 2006.

3   This is mainly government survey data: National AIDS Control Organisation (NACO), *National Behavioural Surveillance Survey 2006*.

4   CD4 (Cluster of Differentiation 4) cells protect the body's immune system. The number of CD4 cells per cubic millilitre of blood is a measure of the body's immunity. The range for CD4 count for an HIV negative person is 500–1500.

HIV positive people with a CD4 count above 500 are in good health. Once an HIV positive person's CD4 count goes below 200, the person is diagnosed with AIDS and is highly susceptible to fatal infections.

5   Viral load is the number of HIV particles in a millilitre of blood. It is a measure of the progression of HIV in the body.

6   Brilliantly depicted in the Hindi film *Udta Punjab* (2016).

7   Dance bars were banned by the Maharashtra government in August 2005, taking the view that dance performances in bars are obscene and derogatory to women's dignity, giving rise to exploitation of women. Before the ban, more than 100,000 women were employed in some 1400 dance bars in the state. The Mumbai High Court overturned the ban in April 2006, but the Supreme Court ordered that dance bars remain closed until its final decision. In July 2013, the Supreme Court overturned the ban. In the interim years 2005–13, thousands of dance-bar girls lost their livelihoods; many were forced to practise sex work on the streets.

4. The Importance of Brothels

1   The oldest survey available is by the Bombay Municipal Corporation in 1992, which estimated 50,000 sex workers in Kamathipura.

2   Avahan survey data from multiple locations suggested a 'typical' structure in India of sex work as being roughly 70–75 per cent street-/lodge-based, 20–25 per cent home based, and 5–10 per cent brothel-based. This would vary of course by location.

3   Narat Punyacharoensin and Chukiat Viwatwongkasem, *Trends in Three Decades of HIV/AIDS Epidemic in Thailand by Nonparametric Backcalculation Method*, March 2016 (ISSN 0269-9370); UNAIDS/WHO, *Epidemiological Fact Sheet on HIV/AIDS and Sexually Transmitted Infections – 2004 Update*.

4   HIV transmission risk can go up by a factor of ten times if one of the partners has an ulcerative STI such as syphilis.

5. The Invisible Consumer

1   This custom of marriage between maternal uncle and niece is mainly practised in traditional Hindu families in parts of southern India (especially in Andhra Pradesh, Karnataka, and Tamil Nadu).

2   A May 2004 report by the National Council of Applied Economic Research, *The Great Indian Middle Class*, categorizes households with an

annual income between 200,000 and one million rupees (at 2001–02 prices) as middle class.

6. Leadership Secrets of the Commercial Sex Worker

1   Sex workers would almost always say that they use condoms every single time. They pick the answer they think the interviewer wants to hear, which tends to happen in behavioural surveys of any kind. There were many different survey and estimation methods that we used to get the truest picture of condom usage in a population. One is the 'mystery client' technique where the surveyor poses as a client. The other is the polling booth method, where answers are dropped anonymously into a sealed ballot box.
2   'Rowdy', though an English word, was the term often used in South India for hooligan. In the northern part of India the term is 'goonda'.

7. Heartbreak in Eden

1   The Armed Forces Special Powers Act (1958) was created to combat insurgency. It allows the military to search and arrest without warrant and use deadly force upon 'reasonable suspicion'. Cases of the military misusing the act and committing atrocities against civilians have fuelled many protests. In July 2004 a team of Assam Rifles men were alleged to have raped and murdered Thangjam Manorama, a thirty-two-year-old Manipuri woman suspected of being a UG member. The incident outraged the entire region, provoking a peaceful protest by thirty elderly Manipuri women, who walked naked to army headquarters, with banners reading, 'Indian Army, rape us'.
2   NACO, 'HIV Sentinel Surveillance and HIV Estimation in India 2007: A Technical Brief,' October 2008.
3   In the United States, for example, use of federal funds for needle exchange programmes has been banned since 1988, with a brief period of reversal between 2009 and 2011.
4   Cited in S. Guin, 'Prison Inmates Living with HIV in India: Case Studies from Prisons in Maharashtra', *Springer Briefs in Criminology*, Springer International Publishing, 2005, as 'Nagaraj, et al., 2000 as cited in Goyer 2003' and 'UNODC 2007; Dolan, et al., 2007'. Very little data is available regarding the prevalence of HIV in Indian prisons. A case study conducted at Mysore jail found that 9.5 per cent of the female inmates had contracted the HIV virus.

8. Seeking Nirvana

1 This word has no close English translation. It roughly means a 'house' or a tradition, defined by its customs. For example, in Indian classical music, the artists belong to various music gharanas.
2 The word aravani is used mainly in Tamil Nadu and some parts of the South, but most transgender people across India believe they are the brides of Lord Aravan.

9. Back at the Ranch

1 Avahan was funding only through NGOs. The Indian government took up that funding when Avahan was over, as explained in chapter 19.

10. Scenic Route

1 NACO, *National Behavioural Surveillance Survey 2006: Female Sex Workers (FSWs) and Their Clients.*
2 Indian Council of Medical Research and Family Health International, *National Summary Report* (December 2009), *Integrated Behavioural and Biological Assessment*, Round 1 (2005–07).

11. Travels with the Foundation

1 The only trip Bill and Melinda made together during my tenure was this first one, in 2005.

12. The Other Mysore

1 NACO and Avahan estimates.
2 In fact, we did this in every state. It was considered radical because the usual practice was to call for, and then evaluate, competitive proposals. That would have taken months. Also, in most cases there was an incumbent agency already doing good work, and we thought it was sensible to just work with them – which was just as well because every agency we selected, seemingly so brashly, did an outstanding job.
3 An article published around that time on the front page of the *Wall Street Journal* ('New Therapy', 3 May 2004) by Marilyn Chase, the paper's senior health writer, may be of interest to readers.

4   This name is difficult to translate. Literally it means 'the lane of an anna and
    a half'. The rupee used to be counted as sixteen annas, each anna being four
    paise. There was never any half-anna coin, but the connotation of the name is
    that the lane was as small and insignificant as an anna and a half.

13. Counting the Numbers

1   Subsequently other methods have come up. PREP (pre-exposure prophylaxis)
    is when one or both partners take an ART tablet before risky sex. Male
    circumcision has been introduced as a public health intervention in Africa. It
    is a question worth asking why men would go to such lengths rather than use
    a condom!
2   Participatory site assessment was one where estimates were gathered for
    different sites from people who know those places well, such as sex workers,
    autorickshaw drivers, and paanwallahs. Another approach was to analyse
    social networks, drawn on large charts, mapping how many members of her
    community each sex worker knew. The estimates using this method were too
    broad to be useful, falling in a range of 2000 to 5000. The problem was that
    the target population was moving continuously, and this kind of static site
    assessment methods would be inaccurate.
3   Some of the sex workers were curious about the formula. The core of it is a
    simple arithmetic of ratios. The idea is that the number of fish caught the first
    time as a percentage of the total in the pond is the same as the percentage of
    marked fish caught in the second haul to the total in the haul. There are some
    assumptions, if the formula is to be relied upon: the area must have a boundary;
    there should not be in or out migration; the population within the area must
    be moving constantly.

        Thinking of sex workers as fish, the city of Mysore as the area, factoring in
    the fact that migration in and out of Mysore was limited, and that sex workers
    were moving within Mysore from site to site – Sushena felt the conditions
    applied at least broadly. She felt it would be 'the best guesstimate'.

        Interestingly, many of the sex workers readily understood how the formula
    worked; the others were happy to go on trust. (I suggest the reader also go on
    trust if you are lost at this stage!)

15. A Place of Their Own

1   Certain STIs, such as syphilis, fuel the transmission of HIV many times over. These STIs are easily treatable, for example, with penicillin.
2   Borrowing the phrase used by the central government, the United Progressive Alliance, to manage its large coalition of political parties.

16. Shahid

1   The Venereal Disease Research Laboratory test is for syphilis, an ulcerative STI that most fuels the transmission of HIV.

17. Fighting Back

1   True to my training I ran the numbers and found that the correlation coefficient (R^2) between incidents of violence and HIV prevalence was significant. And later, as response time to violence came down, the correlation with reported STI cases was very high.
2   Many roles and interventions at Ashodaya had such formal, even technical, names, starting with words such as guides and community consultants. It simplified communicating their work to the outside world, especially potential donors.
3   Almost every police commissioner after Gopalakrishnan supported Ashodaya. This was the result of sustained advocacy work with the police, such as regularly presenting them data on violence and inviting them to preside over major functions.

18. Taking Wing

1   Ashodaya had started providing training to Avahan programmes in different parts of India. It was part of the knowledge exchange process we had started, where programmes were sharing their knowledge with each other.

19. Handing Over

1   The third National AIDS Control Programmeme (NACP3, 2007–12) had a four-pronged strategy: 1. Prevent new infections in high-risk groups and the

general population; 2. Provide care, support, and treatment to a larger number of people living with HIV/AIDS; 3. Strengthen the infrastructure at the district, state and national levels; and 4. Strengthen the nationwide strategic management information system.

2   Swasthi's 'Avahan III 2017 Report' provides a wealth of information on the extent of vulnerability reduction among high-risk groups.

Epilogue

1   Figures pertaining to trends in HIV have to be understood carefully. In the case of India's figures, the following points are important to remember:

(a) The original estimate of 4.8 million infected was revised to 2.1 million in 2006 after a change in methodology.

(b) HIV prevalence is only a rough measure. It can even go *up* as the battle against HIV is won. This is because of the advent of treatment, and the fact that people with HIV will now live much longer lifespans.

(c) The best marker is incidence, not prevalence, which is the number of *new* infections every year. This of course is tough to estimate because who is to say how long ago a person got infected.

(d) For India, regional- and even district-level epidemics are more meaningful to consider than a single national estimate. To give a sense of scale, India could contain more than five hundred Botswanas or seventeen Thailands. A few districts in a state that are high prevalence/incidence could greatly destabilize the state as a whole.

2   All figures are Avahan programme monitoring data.

Appendix

1   UNAIDS/WHO, *Epidemiological Fact Sheet on HIV/AIDS and Sexually Transmitted Infections – 2004 Update.*

2   Ministry of Health, National Centre for HIV/AIDS, Dermatology and STD, *Report on HIV Sentinel Surveillance in Cambodia 2002*; Narat Punyacharoensin and Chukiat Viwatwongkasem, *Trends in Three Decades of HIV/AIDS Epidemic in Thailand by Nonparametric Backcalculation Method*, March 2016 (ISSN 0269-9370); and UNAIDS/WHO, *Epidemiological Fact Sheet on HIV/AIDS and Sexually Transmitted Infections – 2004 Update.*

Acknowledgements

It would not have been possible to make this journey of my life without the help of numerous people who provided guidance and inspiration. It would have been impossible to write this book, a first-time adventure of a different kind, without the support and guidance of several others.

First and foremost, I thank the thousands of sex workers, MSMs, transgender people, injecting drug users, and truckers I was privileged to work with for ten years. I am especially grateful to the several community members I got to know personally, who moved me and taught me many life lessons.

I am deeply grateful to the many members of the Ashodaya family in Mysore who spent considerable time providing valuable inputs. They include Akram, 'Mobile' Pragya, Bhagyamma, Chandan, Charu, Jinu, Kavita, K.T. Venukumar, Pratima, Raghav, Raghu, Shahid, Ratnamma, Sayyed, Shantamma, and Vasuthi Kastur.

Avahan was funded, supported, and guided by the Bill & Melinda Gates Foundation, and I am most grateful to the people who put their faith behind this expedition into the unknown. They could have insisted on a more cautious approach, but they gave us the freedom to experiment responsibly. Thanks to Bill and Melinda, for whom words will never be enough; Helene Gayle for being such an understanding boss; Patty Stonesifer, CEO of the Gates Foundation when we started out, for unstinting support; David Allen, Steff Bertozzi, Nick

Hellmann, Rick Klausner, Luke Nkinsi, Tachi Yamada, Larry Cohen, and Mark Suzman, who supported and guided our work at different stages.

I wish I could personally thank the late John Stewart, my mentor, whose wisdom and wit and ability to say tough things without hurting gave me strength and clarity when I most needed it. I am grateful to Sundar Sundaraman, true Vaishnav jan, from whom I learnt what commitment to the community really means. I will always be thankful to Swarup Sarkar, who first emphasized to us the importance of evidence and mid-course corrections and had answers to every tough technical question. And of course to Sushena Reza-Paul, from whom I learnt what compassion in action looks like, and the many facets of leadership. Throughout Avahan, they were always available to coach and explain, and became my good friends.

The AIDS sector was full of individuals who worked quietly and selflessly for the cause and I am thankful to all of them for the inspiration they always provided. Three stellar examples are Anjali Gopalan, Anand Grover, and Akhila Sivadas, tireless advocates in different ways for the cause of those most vulnerable to HIV.

Thanks to all those who served at various times on Avahan's technical panel, especially Christine Galavotti, Charlie Gilks, Smarajit Jana, Prabhat Jha, Marie Laga, Sheila Mitchell, Rob Moodie, and Richard Steen. My thanks also to Professor Peter Piot, former head of UNAIDS, for all his support and to his succesor Michel Sdibe.

There are numerous individuals who provided leadership from the organizations to which we gave grants, and I am grateful to them. They include D.P. Aggarwal and Vineet Aggarwal, Michelle Andina, John Anthony, Alvaro Bermejo, Parinita Bhattacharjee, James Blanchard, Ties Boerma, Peter Deutschmann, Nidhi Dubey, Sanjeev Gaikwad, the late Parmeshwar Godrej, Manoj Gopalkrishnan, B. Jayakrishnan, the late Dr Katharine Kay, Bob Kelty, Preeti Kumar, R. Lakshmi bai, B. Langkham, Rob Lorway, Yvonne Macphertson, Meera Mishra, H.L. Mohan, Radha Rani Mitra, Stephen Moses, P. Prabhakar, Priyanka Dutt, Kannika Singh, Shumon Sengupta, Carol

Squire, Tom Thomas, Darshana Vyas, and Reynold Washington. Special thanks to Tarun Vij for sharing his memories, and analysis, of Avahan's truckers' programme. Thanks to some key people from Swasthi – Helen, Pushpalata, Shama Karkal, and Shiv Kumar, and the sex workers we interviewed in Parbani.

I am grateful to Tony Bondurant, independent consultant, and Mariam Claesen from the World Bank, for their collaboration. Over ten years we worked with many fine people from USAID and CDC, and I would like to thank those organizations, especially Robert Clay from USAID. Thanks to P. Kousalya and K.K. Abraham, leaders of PNP and INP, the HIV positive people's associations. Among journalists, Sanchita Sharma and Lalita Panicker were steadfast in their support of the cause.

We are fortunate to have worked with some exemplary leaders from central and state governments. They include J.V.R. Prasada Rao and K. Sujatha Rao, who both led NACO with both head and heart at critical junctures, and then provided support after they each became Union Health Secretary. Vandana Gurnani made a big difference when leading the Karnataka AIDS Control Society, and then in establishing the Karnataka Health Promotion. I am grateful to K. Damayanthi for her leadership and support to us when we worked with the Andhra Pradesh State AIDS Control Society.

A deeply committed nine-member National Technical Support Unit (NTSU) played a vital role in the process of transition of Avahan to government. I am grateful to all of them, especially Deepak Dobhal and Senthil Murugan.

My special thanks to the public figures who lent their time and influence to Avahan, and made a big difference – Vishwanathan Anand, Rahul Dravid, Richard Gere, and Kamal Hassan. I am grateful to the pre-eminent authors who contributed to *AIDS Sutra*, including William Dalrymple, Kiran Desai, Salman Rushdie, Vikram Seth, and Professor Amartya Sen.

My core Avahan team never exceeded sixteen people, but there would have been many more who joined and left Avahan at different

times. They are Alkesh Wadhwani and Debbie Seymour with whom
I started the journey, Negar Akhavi, Aparajita Bhalla, Manisha
Bharti, Padma Chandrasekaran, Gina Dallabetta, Jacquelline Fuller,
Shivanshu Gupta, Matangi Jayaram, Narendra Kande, Usha Kiran,
Sonia Kumar, Sameer Kumta, Virginia Loo, Hari Menon, James
Moore, Jonty Rajagopalan, Aparajita Ramakrishnan, Penny Richards,
Sema Sgaier, Nishant Sharma, Amit Soni, Deepti Tanuku, Shelley
Thakral, Reenu Uppal, Vasanti Vepa, and Tisha Wheeler – I hope
this book brings back some of those good times, guys!

I am grateful to the staff and community members from Life Line
in Durban, South Africa, and of HOYMAS in Nairobi, Kenya, for
taking the time to talk to me about their links with Ashodaya.

I am grateful to Rob Guth for his mentorship and for encouraging
me to write in the first place; Vijay Chibber for explaining the
complexities of the North-East at great length; Marilyn Chase for
recalling those early memories of Ashodaya from her 2004 article for
the *Wall Street Journal*; Karthik Ram, who developed some valuable
background data; Garima Sood for administrative support; Morgan
Witzel for inputs on early drafts; and Sheila Lal for those golden days
in seclusion at Alyndale, enabling the last mile of this book.

I am most grateful to Sumay Gupta for his meticulous reference
research, including travel to field locations to make sure I had certain
details right. Sumay is a perfectionist who exudes calm, which is a rare
phenomenon, and working with him was always a joy.

Thank you Durga Raghunath, for having the first look at my work
in progress and giving me a thumbs up.

Juggernaut's is an all-star team. Thanks Nandini Mehta for your
guidance, encouragement, and always honest feedback. It has been
a privilege working with you. I am grateful to Jaishree Ram Mohan
for her elegant and piercing editorial inputs, to Gavin Morris, and of
course to Chiki Sarkar.

My late parents were always proud of my work and supported me
throughout, though I knew my mother never quite reconciled to all its

aspects! My father's deep commitment to national service somewhere played a part in my embracing my new role.

My wife, Anjali, has spent more than twenty-five years working with Mobile Creches, an NGO based in Delhi that does amazing work for the children of migrant workers on construction sites. Watching her tireless commitment to a good cause made a deep impression on me and played its part in my decision to step out and try to make a difference. Thank you also for your understanding when Avahan took me away.

Thanks to my two sons and their lovely life-partners – Ashwin and Alison, Aman and Sandy – for reviewing this book as it developed and providing so many useful inputs.

It was an arduous campaign, and the list of people who made a difference, and to whom I am grateful, is long. It is quite possible, perhaps inevitable, that I have left some names out. I apologize sincerely to those people.

The views represented here are entirely my own. It goes without saying that if there are any mistakes in this narrative, they are entirely my fault.

1

CRAFTED FOR MOBILE READING

Thought you would never read a book on mobile? Let us prove you wrong.

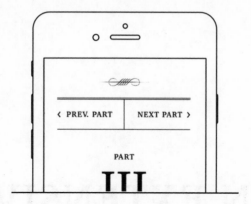

Beautiful Typography

The quality of print transferred
to your mobile. Forget ugly PDFs.

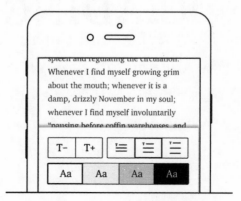

Customizable Reading

Read in the font size, spacing
and background of your liking.

juggernaut.in

AN EXTENSIVE LIBRARY

Including fresh, new, original Juggernaut books from the likes of Sunny Leone, Praveen Swami, Husain Haqqani, Umera Ahmed, Rujuta Diwekar and lots more. Plus, books from partner publishers and loads of free classics. Whichever genre you like, there's a book waiting for you.

juggernaut.in

DON'T JUST READ; INTERACT

We're changing the reading experience from passive to active.

Ask authors questions

Get all your answers from the horse's mouth.
Juggernaut authors actually reply to every
question they can.

Rate and review

Let everyone know of your favourite reads or
critique the finer points of a book – you will be
heard in a community of like-minded readers.

Gift books to friends

For a book-lover, there's no nicer gift than
a book personally picked. You can even
do it anonymously if you like.

Enjoy new book formats

Discover serials released in parts over
time, picture books including comics,
and story-bundles at discounted rates.
And coming soon, audiobooks.

juggernaut.in

4

LOWEST PRICES & ONE-TAP BUYING

Books start at ₹10 with regular discounts and free previews.